THE GENE SHIFTERS

Other titles in the  series:

BUILDING FUTURES

ON THE STREETS

THE GENE

SHIFTERS

JOHN NEWELL

W H ALLEN

First published in Great Britain 1989 by
W. H. Allen & Co Plc
Sekforde House, 175–9 St John Street, London EC1V 4LL

© John Newell 1989

ISBN 1 852 27176 0

Designed by Roger Kohn

Printed and bound in Great Britain by
Mackays of Chatham Plc

CONTENTS

Acknowledgements

My thanks are due to John Tusa and the BBC World Services for always providing a fertile environment to encourage science writing and broadcasting, to Geoff Potter, Maurice Lex and the Biotechnology Directorate of the Science and Engineering Research Council for letting me edit their newsletter. That has brought me constantly into contact with biotechnology and, especially, genetic engineering at the cutting edge.

INTRODUCTION

We used to think of evolution and natural selection as being, while blind and amoral forces, still something which produced splendid creatures, such as ourselves. Homo sapiens sat proudly at the top of the family tree of life, placed there, if not by God, at least by a hard-won supremacy in the struggle for existence. But nowadays scientists talk of evolution more in terms of our genes than of ourselves. Individual humans have been reduced to the status of large, ramshackle, relatively short-lived structures, assembled with the single–minded aim of promoting the survival and spread of the potentially immortal stream of DNA, – deoxyribonucleic acid, the stuff of which our genes are made – flowing on through our offspring.

We fight, it seems, not for our family or our country but for our genes because our family, and our nation to some extent, have similar genes. We are conned into making love, though we don't know it, to propagate those same genes. Once the brutally brief period allowed to prehistoric man for reproduction is over, our aches and pains accumulate. Cancer, arthritis, heart disease, premature senility – our genes don't care. We have done our bit to proliferate them. We can be consigned to the scrap heap.

But now things are changing. Humans, the servants our genes use to ensure their propagation, have become genetic engineers. We have always worked for our genes; now they are being made to work for us.

Genetic engineering involves taking genes from one living

1

organism and shifting them into another; a process which has turned out to be, at least for most purposes, easier than expected and which has therefore progressed rapidly. Genes are made more or less the same in every living thing; a virus, a fungus, an oak tree, a cat, you and me.

Genes have only been shifted between living things for about fifteen years but already gene shifting is routine in labs all over the world. Nowadays genes are not just shifted – they are also manufactured by gene machines, and altered when necessary. Each gene is a blueprint for one of the large molecules which carry out living processes. The blueprint can now be redrawn and we can begin to invent new genes.

To give just one example, the blueprint for human insulin, now being made outside the human body by cell cultures programmed with human genes, has been redrawn, slightly but significantly. Insulin altered in this way, injected by diabetics, is absorbed as quickly as natural insulin, produced by the body. The outcome could be an end to most of the long–term health problems endured by diabetics.

The first genes to be shifted were human genes. They were taken from human cells and put into laboratory cell cultures, so as to programme the cultures to make human substances, for use as medical drugs – to control growth and to combat infection for example.

These substances, of which more later – interferons and the like – are extraordinarily potent by the standards of ordinary pharmacology. They have very big, complex protein molecules, much too big to make by conventional synthetic chemistry. But by shifting human genes into cell cultures, it is possible to make them in any required quantities. Interferon – which turned out to be not one but several substances – and the hormone insulin are among the first human chemicals to have been made in this way. Experts predict that by 2000 AD human control substances – 'clones' as biotechnologists say – will form the majority of medical drugs used against disease.

For plant breeders, gene shifting offers the potential to go much faster and to draw on infinitely more resources than they use today. Conventional breeding means searching for a wild variety of the same species with a wanted characteristic, resistance to disease, say, using the wild variety to fertilize a crop plant and picking out the offspring with the wanted characteristic.

Then there is the long, slow business of breeding out of the offspring all the unwanted characteristics of the wild plant which came in along with the wanted one. That can take many generations. If no wild plant has the wanted characteristics well, that's too bad.

Gene shifting opens up, quite literally, the whole living world to the plant breeder. A gene can be taken from a bacterium, a fungus – even an animal – and inserted into a plant to make it more nutritious or more resistant to disease. The gene goes in on its own – there's no need to put any other genes in with it – so the genetic improvement is accomplished in a single generation.

Although the techniques of gene shifting in plants have been established for a while, genes are only now beginning to be shifted into the plants that matter to people – crop plants. It has proved unexpectedly difficult to get genes into the class of plants from which most economically important crops are drawn. But ways to get them in are being found now and 'green gene' shifting is steaming ahead.

Surprisingly, it's been easier to shift genes into animals than into crops. 'Transgenic' mice, sheep, rabbits and pigs are the result. Giant mice with extra genes for growth hormone were a first product. Now sheep implanted with genes to produce human body control substances are alive and well, in Edinburgh, where scientists have taken the lead in the transgenic animal race. The pharmaceutical farmyard, where cows produce tomorrow's drugs to be profitably filtered out of their milk, will soon be here.

And then of course there's us. Already new genes have been inserted into people. All the required techniques have already been tried in animals and have proved successful. Humans are afflicted by over 2000 diseases caused by defects in single genes, all incurable, many serious, often tragically progressive and remorselessly fatal. But here too we are beginning to turn the tables on our genes. New techniques are pinpointing one by one the genes which become defective in such diseases, so eventually, they can be repaired or replaced.

It is proving difficult to put new human genes into parts of the human body where the native genes are defective and to make them work there, so as to cure genetic disease for an individual. It is, however, proving surprisingly easy to put extra genes into egg cells so that the genes find their way not only into the individual who grows from the egg but also into all his or her descendants, and their descendants for ever. Whether such germ line gene therapy will ever be either necessary or desirable is much debated. What is certain is that it is already possible, though so far it has only been done in mice.

Gene shifters are at work in industry too. At present the numbers of chemical reactions valuable to industry that living cells – or enzymes taken from them – can perform, are limited, and so therefore is the impact of modern biotechnology on chemical industry, apart from pharmacology. But there are clever ways, including genetic engineering, to make living cells and enzymes more potent and even to invent new enzymes. As their power and numbers grow, the advantages of enzymes in chemical industry, working at lower temperatures and pressures and so saving precious energy, will become clearer and clearer. Gene shifters and other biotechnologists will see more and more greening of industry as time goes on.

In this book I have taken each of the areas I mentioned here in turn, and tried to explain how far gene shifting has gone in each of them, and where it may go in the future. There is some duplication because I don't want readers to have to keep flipping from one chapter to another. And I have allowed myself some wild speculation about the far future. Some bits are sure to be embarrassingly out of date by the time the book is published because genetic engineering is moving so fast. I apologize in advance for technical errors, which shouldn't creep in but will because of the sheer size of the field. For those who want to go further into the details of DNA, an explanatory appendix is included. But for what may be seen as over simplification, there and elsewhere I make no apology. The biotechnology revolution is well into its second and highly sophisticated phase now, but as journalist and broadcaster I know that most people worldwide haven't caught up with the first phase yet. Here I hope is a crash course.

1

RECRUITING NATURAL KILLERS

Patrolling your body and mine are microscopic armies of dedicated defenders ready to protect us against every kind of infectious disease and against cancers. These defenders include different classes of white blood cells which recognize and attack foreign invaders in various ways, and numerous chemical messengers, are sent via the blood stream from one white cell which has spotted an invader to others to tell them to join the counter–attack.

As well as sending chemical messages, called lymphokines, some white cells make other chemicals, complex proteins called antibodies. These combine the functions of chemical warfare, pathfinding, and target marking. For example, antibodies attach themselves to foreign organisms – bacteria, viruses or parasites – which have entered the body. They mark them down for further attack by white blood cells, as well as themselves helping to destroy the invaders. Together these armies and agents, white cells, lymphokines and antibodies, make up the human immune system.

Genetic engineering is now making it possible to provide all these natural defenders with reinforcements from outside the body. Using genetic engineering and other techniques, antibodies and lymphokines, chemical weapons, markers and chemical messengers, can all be made outside the body. Then they can be reinjected for any purpose and in any quantities. White cells

5

themselves can now be grown outside the body, given new orders, and sent back into the body to undertake new missions. In these ways resistance to diseases, including cancers, can be strengthened or even created where it does not naturally exist. This chapter looks at our natural defenders, and the ways in which they are being reinforced.

Antibodies are the agents which have been the most widely made and used to date. We are born with the ability to make all the antibodies our bodies will ever need. But the sheer number of different antibodies we can make – something in excess of two million – makes it seem as though antibodies are specially created each time infections, bacteria or viruses, get into our bodies, though in fact the ability to make them is always there awaiting the need.

Some cancer researchers believe that many more cancers start to develop than those which become fully-fledged tumours. They argue that the others are detected and destroyed by the immune system before they have time to grow into detectable tumours. This must involve the formation of antibodies against tumours as part of the process of destruction. Clearly such natural defences are ineffective once tumours are big enough to be detected by doctors. But scientists now hope to use antibodies made outside the body to kill cancers in new ways by directing cell-killing poisons selectively at tumours and away from normal, healthy tissue.

The first requirements for this are antibodies which will react specifically with cancer cells and not with normal cells. These antibodies are needed in very pure form and in sufficient quantities to be used in such therapy. Until 1975 antibodies could only be obtained from human blood, in tiny quantities and, inevitably, in impure mixtures. Then Doctors Caesar Milstein and George Kohler of the Medical Research Council's Molecular Biology laboratory at Cambridge announced their success in making what are called monoclonal antibodies – the achievement for which they were later awarded a Nobel Prize.

Monoclonal antibodies are made by injecting mice for example with whatever an antibody is required to react with, say, human cancer cells. The mice then make antibodies against the proteins, antigens on the cancer cells' surfaces. Then the cells making the antibodies are removed from the mice and fused with other cells which grow and divide vigorously. This creates a hybrid cell culture, a hybridoma, which will grow to any required size and go on producing as much of the anti-cancer antibody as is required, indefinitely. The process of making the cells producing antibodies into hybridomas immortalizes the production of the antibody.

Monoclonal antibodies have a host of uses in modern medicine and medical research. The making of monoclonal antibodies is nearly as important in medical biotechnology as the shifting of genes from one living thing to another – the recombining of DNA. Recombinant DNA and monoclonal antibodies are the two keys to the success of modern biotechnology; they will be found in partnership throughout this book.

The making of monoclonal antibodies was first reported in August 1975. One of the first experimental uses to which the antibodies were put was in trying to target cell-killing toxins selectively to cancer tumours. Since then genetic engineers have taken this still-experimental therapy into a second generation of more sophisticated medical guided missiles.

Monoclonal antibodies made against human cancer tissue can be produced in relatively large quantities, and joined chemically to potent cell-killing toxins. Among the toxins used are ricin, a plant poison (used by the Bulgarian assassin who killed Georgi Markov with a poisoned umbrella), the diphtheria toxin made by diphtheria bacteria, and radioactive isotopes producing radiation which is deadly at very short range.

If such deadly materials were injected into the body with no targetting mechanism, they would cause as much damage to normal, healthy tissue as to cancer cells. But when toxin molecules are joined to monoclonal anti-cancer antibodies then, as the antibodies come into contact with and bind to cancer cells, the toxin accumulates on the surface of the tumour and poisons it. This targetting effect means that much higher doses can be used without damage to normal, healthy tissue, giving a better chance of eliminating all the cancer tissue, and curing the patient. The same technique is also being used to locate tumours by concentrating detectable radiation in them.

This leads us to one of the latest and most exciting uses of genetic engineering in medicine – solving the problem of these anti-cancer antibodies being rejected by a patient's immune system. The fact that the anti-cancer antibody is made by cells from mice, fused with other cells in hybridomas, has severely limited the use of antibodies linked to toxins, so-called conjugates, in treating cancer. A mouse antibody is mouse tissue, not human tissue. So when the mouse antibodies are injected into human cancer patients they are recognized as foreign and may be rejected, attacked and destroyed by the patient's immune system.

This often happens within a week or so of injection. It limits the application of monoclonal antibodies in therapy to a single use, because once the antibodies have been recognized and rejected once, they are remembered for ever by the human immune system. If similar antibodies conjugated to toxins are used to treat cancer again in the same patient, they will be destroyed immediately – before they have time to fasten on to the tumour and attack it. A treatment which can be used only once has very limited value.

Research carried out by Dr Greg Winter of the Medical Research Council's Laboratory for Molecular Biology at Cambridge and Dr Herman Waldman of the Cambridge University Department of Pathology has shown how to overcome this problem. What they have done is to disguise mouse monoclonal anti-cancer antibodies as human antibodies. They have injected these disguised antibodies into cancer patients and shown that the antibodies attack the cancer without being recognized as foreign and rejected. (In this particular cancer there is no need to conjugate the antibodies to toxins. The antibodies alone can cause the killing of cancer cells.)

The same technique of using monoclonal antibodies made in mice but disguised as human antibodies is now being applied to treat other diseases. Greg Winter's team has made a crucial breakthrough needed to exploit monoclonal antibodies in medicine.

Their achievement involved not only shifting genes around but redesigning them. First, a human cancer cell antigen, was injected into mice, which responded by making an anti-cancer antibody. Then the mouse gene which was the blueprint for the antibody was analysed. The part of the mouse gene which represents the blueprint for making the small part of the antibody which reacts with the cancer antigen was identified. Then, this small part of the mouse gene was cut out of the rest of the gene, and inserted into a space created for it in a human gene. The space was made by cutting the equivalent bit out of the gene for a human antibody.

The outcome is a gene which makes an antibody which is 99 per cent human and which fastens itself to cancer cells. This gene was inserted into bacteria, *Eschericia coli* (*E. coli* for short) so as to make the hybrid antibody. Cultures of *E. coli* are used to grow many human genes. The human genes take control of the bacteria and make them create all kinds of human body substances for which the genes are the blueprints. This process is called cloning. Cloning human genes and their products in *E. coli* is routine genetic engineering, and has been for several years.

Part of the bacterium's own genome (the sum total of all its genes) is contained in plasmids, little rings of genetic material which are easily and frequently naturally exchanged between bacteria. With the aid of enzymes acting as genetic scissors, genetic engineers are able to cut a plasmid ring open and splice into it an extra gene, a human gene. Then they transfer the plasmid to a bacterium. The bacterium grows and divides and every new bacterium formed contains a duplicate set of genetic material, including the human gene, because all the genes in it are duplicated at each division. All these bacteria will produce the human gene's product, a human protein, just as they produce bacterial proteins according to the instructions of their own genes. The larger the colony of *E. coli* grows, the more of the human protein it will make.

Because bacteria grow very fast and can be grown very cheaply, and because *E. coli* was already widely used for genetic experiments before the advent of genetic engineering, *E. coli* is today the organism most widely used for cloning genes and their products. But because the language of DNA is universal and a gene from any organism will work – with a bit of assistance – in any other organism, genes can be cloned in any kind of cell culture. Today they are being cloned in human and animal cells grown in culture, in yeasts and even as we shall see, in viruses which infect insects.

Greg Winter inserted the hybrid gene, for a human antibody with a mouse reactive site, into *E. coli* via a plasmid and cloned the gene and its product – the corresponding hybrid antibody. The culture produced enough antibody to test in a human patient suffering from a form of leukaemia, T-cell leukaemia. (Leukaemia is cancer of the white cells of the blood and T-cell leukaemia is cancer of one sub-class of white cells, the T-cells.) T-cell antigens were injected into the mouse which made the original monoclonal antibodies, resulting in anti-T-cell antibodies.

Previous treatments using conventional chemotherapy had failed because the leukaemic cells became resistant to it. Mouse monoclonal antibodies made against T-cells had at first been successful in killing leukaemic cells. But after a while the mouse antibodies had been recognized as foreign and had been rejected and destroyed, and after that the treatment was useless.

The humanized antibodies, however, had so little mouse material in them that they were not recognized as foreign, and doctors were able to go on using the antibody until all the leukaemic T-cells had been destroyed. The leukaemia had disappeared. Because such conditions often return after an apparent cure, such patients cannot be pronounced cured for years yet. But the doctors are optimistic.

T-cell leukaemia is only one of several conditions for which antibody treatment looks very promising. The Medical Research Council has licensed the humanizing technique to a number of British pharmaceutical companies to use to treat several conditions. The pharmaceutical company Celltech, for example, plans to make them to treat septic shock, caused by severe bacterial infections in patients who have undergone surgery, a condition which kills 125,000 patients worldwide every year. Celltech's humanized antibodies will neutralize the toxins which are released by bacteria and cause the symptoms of shock.

Unilever plan to use humanized antibodies to diagnose and treat cancer. Because of the antibodies' ability to concentrate radioactive isotopes linked to them around a tumour, these anti-cancer antibodies can be used to locate tumours. Gamma ray cameras pick up and image the 'hot spots' of harmless radiation produced by clustering antibodies on tumours.

Another company, Scotgen of Aberdeen are making humanized antibodies to use against cytomegalovirus infections, which can be fatal to patients with immunity depressed after transplant surgery or by AIDS.

The pharmaceutical company the Wellcome Foundation plan to make humanized antibodies to prevent the rejection of transplanted organs, as well as to treat leukaemia. Since rejection is brought about by particular classes of white blood cells recognizing a transplanted organ as foreign and attacking it, humanized antibodies made to attack only the class of white cells responsible for rejection could prevent this.

There are many other potential uses for humanized monoclonal antibodies, and other research teams besides Greg Winter's are developing them. It has been suggested that tropical parasitic diseases could be attacked with humanized antibodies by directing them against antigens on the surfaces of parasites.

Drug addicts undergoing treatment could benefit too, Dr Winter believes. 'In the plasma of addicts' says Winter, 'there are various noxious chemicals floating about. If we could put into such people a large dose of an antibody which binds to these chemicals then we might be able to flush them out. It may even be possible to make an antibody which not only binds to such drug residues but actually chews them up and detoxifies them in the process.'

For some diseases, such as T-cell leukaemia, monoclonal antibodies against whatever causes the disease, and humanized antibodies in particular, can be effective treatments. Such antibodies can sometimes set off chain reactions which kill the bacterium, cancer cells or whatever is causing the illness. But for other conditions, a monoclonal antibody alone won't be enough – it has to be linked to a toxic killer. Each antibody molecule has to be linked – conjugated – to a molecule of a deadly cell-killing toxin, such as diphtheria toxin, one molecule of which can kill a living cell, or ricin, a fatal plant poison. Such conjugates are medical guided missiles, with the antibody providing the guidance system and the toxin the warhead.

The first such guided missiles to be made and tested in patients have been made chemically, using ordinary chemical processes – as opposed to genetic engineering – to link warhead and guidance system, toxin and antibody. But this has major disadvantages. Toxin and antibody have to be made separately, purified and then linked together. This slow and expensive business often goes wrong, resulting in a conjugate in which the two parts are joined together wrongly, so that the antibody no longer targets its warhead to the cancer cell, or the warhead itself – the toxin – is no longer deadly.

Another group of genetic engineers has found a way round this problem. Instead of producing two separate elements – antibody and toxin – they make the 'guided missile' molecule in one go.

A team led by Dr Michael Neuberger in the Cambridge Laboratory for Molecular Biology, with Dr Michael Lord of Warwick University, Philip Thorpe of the Imperial Cancer Research Fund's labs in London and Ellen Vitetta of the University of Texas have spliced the two genes – the gene for the antibody and the gene for

11

the toxin – together to make a single gene a blueprint for a complete medical guided missile.

They then inserted the blueprint into cell cultures. The cells have accepted its instructions and have produced all-in-one guided missile molecules. Soon they will be tested in human patients as a treatment for cancer.

The history of the project shows not only how genetic engineering and monoclonal antibodies make a formidable combination but also how their application cuts across conventional boundaries between scientific subject areas. It exemplifies the excitement gripping men and women who are aware of the power of the technologies they command. The scientists involved met on the international conference circuit after reading of each others work, and realized they had the complementary skills needed to make medical guided missiles. They decided to team up and work together till the project was finished. For some of them it meant not just inconvenience but a substantial loss of income. One day a great many cancer and other patients may have reason to thank them for it. 'We feel', says Ellen Vitetta, 'that this should go as efficiently and effectively as we can get it to go. And I think this is very exciting because the interaction with one's colleagues is really what we're all in this profession for.'

Now, fourteen years after Milstein's and Kohler's letter in *Nature* first described the making of monoclonal antibodies, they are being made to order to attack any required disease. They are being humanized to avoid rejection and to enable them to be used for long periods in therapy. And the antibodies are being engineered into medical guided missiles to direct cell-killing drugs against cancer, invading bacteria or parasites. A combination of the 'guided missile' and 'humanizing' techniques described above may make a massive impact on cancer, though it is too early to be certain.

Meanwhile, another use for humanized monoclonal antibodies is appearing on the horizon. This is the treatment of auto-immune conditions – diseases in which symptoms are caused by a patient's immune system mistaking part of his or her own body for a foreign invader, and attacking and destroying or damaging that part of the body. Auto-immune conditions include rheumatoid arthritis, multiple sclerosis, thyroid disease and forms of diabetes.

Each auto-immune disease is caused not by the whole immune system making the error but by one small part of it, one sub-class of cells as it were, dropping its bombs on its home territory. By making monoclonal antibodies against such sub-classes, it is now possible to 'take out' all the auto-immune white cells that are causing a harmful reaction, leaving the rest of the immune system intact to continue its work fighting infections and warding off cancer.

The auto-immune disease multiple sclerosis is being treated experimentally in this way by Dr Howard Weiner of the Center for Neurological Disease at the Brigham and Women's Hospital in Boston. It is too early to talk about results, but it is now possible to identify the particular class of cells responsible for the auto-immune reaction that damages the protective sheaths around nerves and so is responsible for the symptoms of multiple sclerosis. Making monoclonal antibodies against these cells and injecting them into MS patients to kill the harmful cells without affecting the rest of the immune system is one way to use these discoveries.

Another way of tackling auto-immune diseases may be to stimulate the patient's own immune system to attack the sub-class of white cells responsible for the disease, by vaccinating him or her with such cells or with an extract from them. The human immune system itself is normally able to recognize and eliminate sub-classes of white cells which are causing auto-immune reactions – they are, so to speak, executed on charges of high treason. When auto-immune disease occurs the watchdogs responsible for this have clearly failed. But they can be reminded of their duties.

Professor Irun Cohen of the Weizmann Institute of Science in Israel has found a way to do this. He identifies errant white cells that cause multiple sclerosis-like symptoms in rats, grows these cells outside the body, kills them and injects them back into the rats. The effect is to remind the watchdogs of their duty. The rat's immune system eliminates not only the injected white cells but also all the others of the same type that are causing the MS-type symptoms in the rat. The disease disappears.

This treatment is now being tried on a few cases of very serious multiple sclerosis in humans. What works in rats often doesn't work in human – it may be useless, or may cause unacceptable side effects. But the hope is there. And such vaccines may be improved by using genetic engineering. Only a small part of any one of the white cells causing the harmful auto-immune reaction does the damage. This part – called the receptor – is also the part which enables the immune system to pick out the cells involved from among other white cells. It is the part which is unique and therefore recognizable.

It is possible to identify the genetic blueprint, the DNA, for the receptor, and to clone just that bit of DNA to make the receptor on its own. Then cloned receptor material can be collected and used as a vaccine. This may be more effective and perhaps easier to make than a vaccine made from complete cells. Cloning is simpler than growing cells, and receptor material will stimulate protective immunity more strongly.

Such techniques are only in their infancy. But many medical researchers believe that the use of monoclonal antibodies or cloned vaccines to destroy, or to stimulate the patient's immune system to destroy the cells causing auto immune reactions will eventually be the treatment used not only for multiple sclerosis, but for rheumatoid arthritis and auto immune thyroid disease.

The combination of monoclonal antibodies and genetic engineering has created several new and promising therapies. But they may soon be overshadowed by another product of genetic engineering – the cloning of lymphokines.

2
CLONING
CHEMICAL MESSENGERS

Lymphokines are the chemical messengers produced by the human body to control the activities of the immune system. Just as the ability to immortalize the making of antibodies has made the large-scale use of antibodies in therapy possible, so the ability to clone human body substances in cell cultures makes the use of lymphokines in therapy possible.

Although the details of lymphokine cloning are complex, the basic technique is simple. In the words of Professor Mike Dexter of the Paterson Laboratories in Manchester, an important centre for research in this field, 'We take the gene which codes for the protein, the lymphokine we are interested in and we cut it out of the normal cell. We insert this gene into something like a bacterium [usually *E. coli*] which will go on to produce large amounts of the protein, much larger amounts than the cells would normally produce. After this we can take the protein produced by these bacteria and purify it, and using this approach, we can make gram quantities of these lymphokines.'

A gram may not sound much. But lymphokines are so potent that a single gram is enough to treat thousands of patients. This potency is because, unlike conventional drugs, the molecule of a lymphokine acts on just one part of a target cell's surface – rather like a key turning a lock. Conventional drugs have more diffuse effects. One molecule of a lymphokine may be enough to trigger a chain reaction in a target cell, which results in that cell becoming, for example, able to recognize and attack cancer cells. The chain reaction amplifies the effect of the lymphokine enormously.

Fifteen lymphokines are now known. The first to be discovered, cloned and used in therapy was interferon, which turned out to be not one but several substances, with different functions. Since then several other lymphokines have been cloned, each of which stimulates the immune system in a different way and each of which, undoubtedly has several functions, some of which are not yet known. But some of these substances have already begun to be used experimentally in medicine, usually for the treatment of cancer; Dr Stephen Rosenberg, Head of Surgery in the American National Cancer Institute has been using a combination of a lymphokine called Interleukin 2 – which stimulates white blood cells to fight cancer – and white blood cells of the immune system themselves, to treat cancers, with some encouraging results. He comments, 'It's a technique which is basically divided into four parts. First we remove white cells from the cancer patient's blood, using a special machine which returns the blood to the patient. Second, we culture these white cells in the laboratory and stimulate them with lymphokines which transform them into "natural killer" cells which are capable of recognizing and destroying cancer tissue. Thirdly, we take these cells and reinject them back into the patient whence they came. And fourthly we administer the lymphokine called Interleukin 2 to the patient. It stimulates the killer cells to go on attacking the tumour.'

Several other groups are now using the same technique, known as the use of LAK – Lymphokine-Activated Killer – cells. In two cancers which do not respond well to conventional treatments, advanced renal (kidney) cancer and malignant melanoma (the most frequently fatal form of skin cancer) LAK treatment has produced response rates better than other therapies.

In the latest elaboration of the technique, LAK cells have been replaced with white cells taken from tissue samples from the patient's tumour, known as tumour infiltrating lymphocytes (TILs). These were cultured outside the body after the TILs had been isolated from the tumour tissue. This technique, which selects the cells which naturally attack tumours most forcefully, has given encouraging results in treating cancer, but it's too early to say just how valuable it will be.

Interleukin 2 was the first lymphokine other than interferon to be cloned and used clinically. It is the only one of the seven known interleukins – the name for chemicals which carry messages between white cells – for which clinical trials are well advanced. But lymphokine therapy is now beginning to take off. The others; numbers 1,3,4,5,6 and 7, have known functions which include stimulating different classes of white blood cells to attack invading micro-organisms and stimulating bone marrow, where new white cells are formed, to produce more such cells.

Two of these interleukins are now entering clinical trials; one will soon enter clinical trials; and three are undergoing preliminary tests on patients (required to establish the best way to use new drugs before starting clinical trials). These tests will help to establish all the various functions of the interleukins.

One thing which is already clear is that when these 'Superdrugs' – as lymphokines are already being called – do come into use, while they will be more potent and more specific than the drugs of today, they will not be without side effects. Far from it. Each lymphokine has more than one function. Doctors will have to accept at least some of the unwanted, equally potent side effects along with the wanted ones. Even in the world of superdrugs there will be no such thing as a perfect drug.

Another group of substances being cloned and used in cancer therapy are the interferons. Interferon, once thought to be a single substance is now known to come in three main forms – alpha, beta and gamma interferon – each of which contains further variations. The interferons have been in use longer than the interleukins. Alpha interferon has been approved for full-scale clinical use against leukaemia and genital warts and is looking promising as a treatment for other cancers; beta interferon is undergoing clinical trials for cancers; and gamma interferon is starting trials against various infectious diseases. Gamma interferon can stimulate one class of white cells, macrophages, to attack the parasites that cause malaria and the bacilli that cause leprosy.

The most recent group of chemical messengers to be cloned and used experimentally in medicine are the so-called Colony Stimulating Factors,(CSFs) As their name implies, these stimulate colonies of cells to grow, in particular stem cells in bone marrow, the cells that make new blood cells. As stem cells grow and divide new white blood cells are budded off them and into the blood stream. Colony stimulating factors speed up this process. Two of them have been cloned at the time of writing. They speed up the production lines on which new white cells are made, and so strengthen immunity.

Conventional cancer chemotherapy attacks all fast-dividing cells, not only cancer cells. Stem cells in bone marrow, which divide constantly to replenish the population of short-lived blood cells, are vulnerable to cancer chemotherapy. This is the main limitation on the doses that can be used in such therapy and so are the chances of it achieving a cure. CSFs will, it is hoped, be used to help cancer patients rebuild their bodies' populations of white cells after chemotherapy. CSFs could also help AIDS patients to counter the steady destruction of white cells from which the disease gets its name, Acquired Immune Deficiency Syndrome, by increasing the rate at which new cells are produced to replace those lost to the disease.

CSFs could also help leukaemia patients, who can sometimes be treated by destroying their own, cancerous bone marrow and replacing it with grafts of a near relative's healthy marrow. Until the new bone marrow has become established, the patient is deficient in white cells and so in immunity and therefore vulnerable to all infections. CSFs could speed up the growth of new bone marrow and bring forward the time when the patient acquires a complete new healthy immune system.

The lymphokines; interleukins, interferons, colony stimulating factors – and the others still to be discovered – between them seem likely to improve the treatment of most cancers and many infectious diseases. Until it became possible, through genetic engineering, to isolate the human genes for such substances, insert them into laboratory cell cultures and clone the genes and their products, none of the wealth of new therapies described above – and the far greater number which will follow them before the end of the next century – would have been possible at all.

The speed with which lymphokines have been cloned is remarkable, but it is also true that plain, unadorned lymphokines are only the beginning of the story. As with antibodies, genetic engineers are already improving on nature.

We've already seen that, since lymphokines have such potent beneficial effects, their unwanted or harmful side effects are likely to be equally potent. Ideally, lymphokines should be targeted to the tumour, the site of infection or wherever they are needed and kept out of contact with the rest of the body as far as possible, so as to avoid these side effects. It makes sense to use antibodies to direct lymphokines to their targets just as antibodies are being used to direct toxins to tumours, as we've just seen. So monoclonal antibodies made against tumours or viruses are being linked to molecules of, in the first place, interferon. First tests of these conjugates have shown that antibodies are effective in targetting interferon to attack viruses or cancer cells.

As with other 'guided missiles' the next step will be to combine the gene for the antibody and the gene for interferon into one single gene and then to clone this. Monoclonal antibodies offer the potential to deliver lymphokines to chosen sites in the body for most purposes, avoiding side effects on other parts of the body and so allowing these potent agents to be used more freely as drugs.

3

REFORMED CANCERS?
REGROWN HEARTS?

With several lymphokines now being used clinically for different purposes, albeit still experimentally, and lymphokine targetting under development, it is possible to look at some of the future uses to which other lymphokines and cloned human body control substances may eventually be put.

In the last year or two it has become increasingly clear that cancer is very often the outcome of an upset in a balance between the effects of two sets of genes; genes which in one way or another accelerate growth, and genes which in one way or another put a brake on it. To be more precise, there are genes for growth factors – substances which stimulate cell growth and division – and genes for the various parts of the receptors through which growth factors stimulate cells to grow. Defects in these genes can lead to excess of growth factors, or to growth factors being made in the wrong place at the wrong time, or to receptors being made defectively so they behave as if they were being stimulated with growth factors when they are not. All these defects can over-stimulate cells to grow and divide when they should not, thus forming tumours.

Cancer is not simply a matter of an upset in a normal balance between opposed sets of genes. Our genes don't doom us to cancer, but they can make us much more susceptible to the environmental factors which cause cancer.

21

Normally we have two copies of each gene in every cell of our bodies, one in each of each pair of chromosomes – the microscopic rods in which our genes are arranged in our cells. But sometimes an inherited defect or a random mutation during a person's lifetime leaves him or her with only one copy of a gene in a cell or cells. If this gene is the gene for, say, a growth controlling substance, then the person is still all right. The single gene can still make enough of the control substance to keep cell division under control. But suppose something else deletes the remaining gene – tobacco smoke in the lung, for example, tobacco smoke being a well-known mutagen, an agent causing gene damage. If this happens the cell will be left with no control over growth and division at all. It will grow and divide uncontrollably and form a tumour.

There is growing evidence to support the idea that many common cancers are caused by this sequence of events, and gene cloning techniques have played an important part in the research involved. The next logical step is to see whether it is possible to stop the growth of cancers by replacing the missing genes or their products in the cancerous cells that lack them. The gene responsible for making the known growth control substance is known as the RB gene, because the first cancer shown to be caused by the absence of the gene was Retinoblastoma, a cancer of the eye. Since then missing RB genes have been shown to be at least partly responsible for some cancers of the breast, lung, colon and rectum. In animal experiments, RB genes implanted into tumours have been shown to stop their growth.

Human bone cancer cells implanted into mice with natural resistance to cancer normally grow into tumours and kill the mice. But when the bone cancer cells had RB genes implanted into them (by inserting the genes into a virus which was then allowed to infect the cells), the bone cancer cells no longer grew into tumours. By producing growth control factors, the RB genes had converted the cancer cells back into normal cells with growth under control again.

Could this kind of genetic engineering be used to cure human cancers, making their cells reform and behave like normal cells by inserting growth control genes into them? Researchers at the University of California at San Diego are now trying to find ways to insert RB genes into tumours inside mice. If they succeed and if the genes stop the growth of the tumours, clinical trials of RB genes as a means of stopping the growth of human cancers could begin in a year or two. But it will be a lot longer before doctors know exactly how effective the treatment is. If the technique for inserting the genes fails to insert them into just one single cancer cell, that cell alone, without the 'brake' of the RB gene, could soon divide and grow into a new tumour.

Nonetheless, genetic engineering is showing the way to new, more logical, more specific and more hopeful therapies for cancers. Another approach could be to use the growth control substance made by the RB gene itself as a form of chemotherapy for cancer, without inserting the genes. This could be a quicker and simpler form of therapy. The extraordinary speed with which the genetic basis of cancer has emerged in the last two or three years suggests that new and better treatments cannot be far behind.

Getting away from cancer, human body control substances which stimulate growth as well as those which suppress it will be used in other branches of medicine as they are identified and cloned. Several such substances are already being intensively researched by university laboratories and biotechnology companies. Known growth factors already cloned include Epidermal Growth Factor (EGF), which promotes the division of skin cells, Platelet Derived Growth Factor (PDGF), which stimulates the division of the cells forming the layers of muscle in the walls of arteries, and Fibroblast Growth Factor (FGF), which stimulates the growth of cells called fibroblasts. These are the cells which form connective tissue, the structural scaffolding which holds the body together. FGF also stimulates the cells which form the inner lining of arteries to grow and divide.

The private American company California Biotechnology (Cal Bio), has succeeded not only in cloning FGF but also in testing cloned FGF in animals and showing that it speeds up the formation of new blood vessels and connective tissue on the sites of wounds. New blood vessels bring supplies of oxygen and nutrients to supply the needs of the fast-growing new tissue which is forming to heal wounds, so FGF speeds wound healing.

Cal Bio see cloned FGF being used in a cream to hasten the healing of burns, ulcers and bedsores. Implanted in capsules which release it slowly, FGF could also speed the healing of internal wounds, including those inflicted in surgery, fractured bones and perhaps damage caused by coronary heart attacks.

23

FGF may also be used to treat brain damage or disease, perhaps including Alzheimers disease. Tests show that FGF makes brain and nerve cells grow and divide; and that it may encourage the regrowth of normal brain tissue to replace that lost in degenerative brain disease.

As more specific growth factors are discovered, it may become possible to grow new organs or parts of organs to replace those lost through disease, accidents or old age. The heart is one example. Today people with hearts massively damaged by disease need transplants or artificial hearts in order to live. But there are far more heart patients than there are accident victims available to provide them with new healthy hearts, and artificial hearts pose endless – and perhaps ultimately insoluble – problems through the incompatibility of living and mechanical components.

Artificial hearts or heart transplants are needed when the cells in adult heart tissue, like those in adult brain tissue, no longer divide so the heart cannot grow to repair defects. But recently it has been discovered that adult brain tissue can be stimulated to grow and divide. In June 1988, twenty-five scientists from several nations met at Rockefeller University in the USA to discuss the possibility of stimulating heart tissue to do the same thing.

Although this research is still at an early stage, the scientists concerned predict the emergence of strategies to use genetic engineering to treat heart disease in new ways. In a coronary heart attack a blockage – partial or complete – of one or another of the branches of a coronary artery supplying the heart muscle with food and oxygen cuts off the supply. Over a period of several days the part of the heart muscle deprived dies and the muscle disintegrates. Then, three or four days later, fibroblasts, cells which form connective tissue, invade the muscle and make scar tissue, to fill the gap left by dead, disintegrating muscle.

The delay in this response provides an opportunity to intervene using cloned agents made outside the body; to stop the formation of scar tissue and instead to stimulate the growth of new heart muscle to fill the gap. But to do this a way must be found to stimulate heart muscle cells to grow and divide as they did when the heart was very young.

Lymphokines which could be used to stop fibroblasts invading the heart have already been discovered. Dr William Claycomb, of the Louisiana State University Medical Center in New Orleans, has found that the growth-promoting and growth-suppressing substances described earlier which are involved in cancer can also regulate growth in adult heart muscle cells, when such cells are grown in laboratory cultures. While in cancer research the long-term aim is to find substances which will suppress cell division, in work on heart disease the search is for substances which will make cells that don't normally grow and divide start to do so.

One lymphokine could delay the invasion by fibroblasts and so prevent the formation of scar tissue. Meanwhile, a sample of healthy heart muscle cells could be taken from the patient, grown in the laboratory, and stimulated with a second lymphokine, a growth promoter, to make the heart muscle cells revert to youthful behaviour and start to grow and divide again. These rejuvenated cells would then be replaced in the heart, to grow and divide to repair the damage.

All this is only beginning to look possible. But the outcome could be a treatment for heart disease which avoids both the problem of rejection involved in heart transplants and that of incompatibility in the use of artificial hearts.

The potential for the use of the body's natural control substances in medicine – interleukins, interferons, growth hormones etc – is barely beginning to be realized, let alone used. Their exploitation depends upon genetic engineering, on the ability to move genes from one organism to another. The genes for the vital substances are now being identified for the first time, and the resulting substances cloned and tested outside the body. Some of them, probably the most important substances, work by stimulating or repressing more genes, so those genes too are now being cloned and their effects investigated in isolation outside the body. In this way the interplay between genes is being dissected and both genes and control substances are beginning to be used in therapy.

As genetic engineering progresses it will be used to alter the control substances to make them more effective for medical purposes. Some will be made all in one piece by hybrid genes, with appropriate monoclonal antibodies built in to direct them to the part of the body where their effect is needed, increasing the effect of a given dose and reducing side-effects.

We have seen how scientists hope to switch off uncontrolled growth and division and how they hope to switch on growth to repair damage after brain or heart disease. The idea could be taken much further. Only a small proportion of the genes in any living cell are 'switched on' at any given time. Only a small proportion of them are being expressed, that is the proteins the genes are the blueprints for are actually being made, at any one time. The rest of the genes are suppressed. Now that the general way in which genes are switched on or off is known, the rate at which the substances which switch specific genes on or off are identified should accelerate. As scientists become able to wake up and switch on the 'silent majority' of inactive genes in our cells, they will acquire new powers to change our cells – and our bodies.

One group of genes being intensively studied are those which control the development of structures such as limbs in insects. Simple defects in such genes make insects grow an antenna where they should grow a leg. This suggests that the development of complete limbs and perhaps organs is under quite simple genetic controls, in insects. Recent work has shown that such controls may be surprisingly similar in humans. Shall we ever be able to reactivate genes which have been silent and suppressed since infancy, so as to regrow, at first perhaps fingers or toes, later whole limbs, finally even organs lost in accidents, warfare or surgery? It is no longer an impossibility.

4

OUTWITTING
PARASITES

Genetic engineering is commonly thought of as a high-tech business which will benefit the rich nations of the world but which is likely to widen the gap between underdeveloped and developed nations. However, if international agencies continue to fund the research needed, and if ways can be found to finance its exploitation, genetic engineering could make its biggest contribution to health and prosperity in the world's poorest countries.

This can be done in agriculture by engineering crops to make them naturally resistant to drought and disease and perhaps even naturally able to fix nitrogen, to obtain this vital element from the air, doing away with the need for expensive fertilisers, herbicides and pesticides. (See 'The Green Genes'.) In medicine, it can be done by making vaccines to protect against the parasitic diseases which are the scourges of the tropics; malaria, schistosomiasis (bilharzia), filariasis (worm infections), trypanosomiasis (sleeping sickness), leishmaniasis and Chagas' disease. (The last two are conditions caused by the trypanosome parasites which are very common in the Middle East and Latin America respectively.)

Medical staff are in short supply in many areas where such diseases are endemic, and drug treatments fail to eliminate the diseases because people are continually being reinfected. Meanwhile, resistance to the drugs develops in the disease organisms and the insects or other creatures that spread infection become resistant

27

to pesticides, and return after elimination campaigns.

Vaccination involves injecting someone with dead or weakened disease organisms. This stimulates the immune system to recognize and attack the disease organism involved. If the same person is subsequently infected with live disease organisms, then their immune system 'remembers' the vaccination and immediately attacks and destroys the invader before it can become established. The 'memory' produced by vaccines lasts for different periods with different diseases, but it often protects for several years and some-times for life. Repeated vaccinations at intervals of several months or years require much less medical manpower and effort than the use of drugs. Vaccines alone will not eliminate tropical diseases, but without vaccines other measures are unlikely to succeed.

Until recently it has been impossible to make vaccines to protect against tropical parasitic diseases because the parasites that cause them are so perfectly adapted to life in the human body that they cannot be grown outside the body in culture in the laboratory. Or at least they cannot be grown cheaply and easily in the quantities required to make vaccines for large-scale use.

In the last few years, the coming of genetic engineering has made it possible to bypass the need to grow parasites in culture to make vaccines. Instead, the particular proteins (the antigens) on the surfaces of the parasites which stimulate immune reactions in the human body can be identified. The parasite's genes for such antigens are then identified, and cloned. The cell cultures or cultures of bacteria in which the genes are cloned can be grown on the scale needed to mass-produce the parasite's antigens according to the instructions of the parasite's genes. The parasite's antigen can be collected, purified and used as vaccine to stimulate immunity. In this way vaccines which it is hoped will protect against all the tropical parasitic diseases are being or will be made and tested.

Genetic engineering may make it possible to make vaccines to protect not only against all the tropical parasitic diseases, but also against other infectious diseases, such as leprosy, for which existing vaccines are too expensive or available only in limited supplies and so cannot eliminate the diseases involved. Vaccination is not the whole answer to the hitherto intractable problems of tropical dis-ease. But, used together with public health measures, education in hygiene, the use of new pesticides to attack creatures that spread disease and improved drugs to treat diseases themselves, new cloned vaccines could be the extra weapons that will tip the balance and make it possible to win the war against tropical diseases. Here are some examples.

Hepatitis B is a widespread disease throughout the developing world. In many African and Asian countries the majority of the population has been infected at one time or another and up to 10 per cent are chronically infected. Up to 5 per cent of those infected develop chronic liver disease, and this often leads to liver cancer. Hepatitis B infection is the commonest single cause of liver cancer and a vaccine which protects against the one can protect against the other. Vaccine to protect against hepatitis B is made by collecting virus material from infected blood and using it to make a vaccine. But this process is relatively expensive, and involves the handling of large amounts of highly infective blood.

The world's first vaccine against hepatitis B to be made by genetic engineering was produced by a team led by Professor Ken Murray of Edinburgh University's Department of Molecular Biology, and colleagues at the Microbiological Research Establishment at Porton Down. They reported their success in a letter in *Nature* 3 May 1979, a letter which marked the beginning of a new era of medical genetic engineering as clearly as did Milstein and Kohler's letter describing the making of monoclonal antibodies in August 1975. I shall describe how the vaccine was made fully, because it is more or less how all cloned vaccines since have been made.

First Murray's team took blood from people who were infected with hepatitis B, and extracted virus particles from it. This was a long process; very few people had enough of the virus in their blood stream for it to be collected and the virus was elusive; at that time (1978) even its structure was not properly known. Next, they isolated DNA from the virus particles. Then they chopped up the DNA into individual genes, using 'molecular scissors', the enzymes called restriction enzymes which naturally cut DNA into its separate genes.

The next step was performed for safety's sake in the high-security laboratories at Porton Down, now the Centre for Applied Microbiology and Research responsible for the peaceful study of infectious diseases, which is maintained by the Public Health Laboratory Service. Cultures of *E. coli* were used to clone viral genes because as it was already widely grown in laboratories for the study of bacterial genetics its own genetics were well understood.

Plasmids were then extracted from the *E. coli* bacteria. (Plasmids are ring-shaped pieces of genetic material which bacteria naturally exchange between themselves, in a process roughly equivalent to sexual reproduction.) More DNA-chopping enzymes, the restriction enzymes, were used to cut open the plasmid rings, and then genes taken from the hepatitis B virus were spliced into the plasmids. Finally, the plasmids with the extra viral genes were mixed with cultures of E. coli. Some of the bacteria absorbed the plasmids, as they do when they exchange plasmids naturally.

Then came one of those tense wait-and-sees in which genetic engineering experiments abound. The hope was that the E. coli would express the viral genes along with their own genes. In other words, that the bacteria would make a viral protein, a protein of the type found in the coat of hepatitis B virus particles, in accordance with the instructions of the viral gene inserted into the plasmids.

It worked. Not only were the viral coat proteins produced but, as the E. coli cultures grew and multiplied, the plasmids containing the viral DNA were duplicated at each cell division along with all the bacterium's own genes. The larger the culture grew, the more viral protein it made, showing that cloning had the potential to make viral proteins in the quantities needed to produce vaccines. The protein was extracted, purified and used, first as an experimental, then as a commercial vaccine.

There are other ways of making hepatitis B vaccine, though cloned vaccines are now becoming the cheapest. But cloning has since been used to produce vaccines for other diseases which could not be produced at all without genetic engineering.

Malaria is the most widespread of all infectious diseases, threatening half the world's population, with an estimated 300 million new cases every year. Malaria kills three or four children in Africa alone every minute. Attempts to eliminate the disease with drugs and insecticides to kill mosquitoes have generally failed, because of the development of resistance to drugs, lack of medical manpower, resistance to pesticides and other problems in controlling mosquitoes. Without a vaccine to produce long-term immunity and save medical manpower, it must be doubtful if the disease can ever be brought under control, let alone eliminated. But until recently it has been impossible to make a vaccine to protect against malaria, because Plasmodia, the one-celled parasites which cause the disease, can only be grown with great difficulty outside the human body.

Gene cloning has bypassed the need to grow plasmodia. Cloned vaccines have been made and are now being tested against malaria. The parasite is a devious and resourceful enemy and there are specially tough problems in the way of making such vaccines work. But as the problems appear it is also becoming apparent that genetic engineering can meet their challenge.

Plasmodia have a complicated life cycle. The parasite is injected into the human bloodstream when an infected mosquito sucks human blood. At this stage of its lifecycle it is known as a sporozoite. Within a few minutes the injected sporozoites are carried in the circulating blood to the liver, where they find their way out of the blood and into liver cells. The parasites can remain dormant there indefinitely. Occasionally, they re-emerge in a different form into the bloodstream, where they invade red blood cells, multiply inside them and burst out into the blood again. These 'blood stage' parasites are known as merozoites.

A blood sucking mosquito becomes infected from the parasites in human blood. In the body of the mosquito, the parasite goes through the sexual stage of its life cycle. 'Male' and 'Female' parasites fuse to mix their genes, and then divide to form new parasites with new combinations of genes. Male and female forms of the parasite's life cycle are known as gametocytes.

There are two big problems to overcome in making a cloned vaccine to protect against malaria. One problem, which is discussed in more detail later, is that it is becoming increasingly clear that the single proteins – the single antigens – used in the first malaria vaccines stimulate immunity much less strongly than the complete organisms used in conventional vaccines. It is as if, in order to be convinced of the need to strike back in force, the immune system has to see a lot of an enemy. If it sees only a tiny bit of the enemy, then the immune system is cautious and limited in its response.

The other problem is the complex life cycle of the malarial parasite. If a vaccine is made entirely from antigens taken from sporozoites, the stage of the parasites' life cycle which is injected into the human bloodstream by the mosquito, then the vaccine will only stimulate the immune system to attack sporozoites. It will not stimulate immunity to other stages in the parasite's life cycle because their surface antigens are not the same as those on the sporozoite. The merozoite that proliferates in the bloodstream has surface antigens which differ from those of the sporozoite.

This means that, for a vaccine made from sporozoite antigens to be effective in giving protection, the immunity it stimulates has to be so powerful that the agents of the immune systems, antibodies and white cells, can destroy all the sporozoites injected into the body by a bloodsucking mosquito very quickly. They must be destroyed in the few minutes before the sporozoites reach the sanctuary of the liver cells they hide in, where the parasites are safe from the immune system.

In spite of this, the first two of the first three vaccines to have been made and tested against malaria are composed of sporozoite antigens. The sporozoite vaccines are made by Hoffman la Roche in Switzerland and by Smith Kline and French of the USA (their vaccine was developed at the company's research labs in the UK). The third vaccine is made from merozoite, blood stage antigens and is made by the British Wellcome Foundation, a group with a long and distinguished record in combating tropical diseases.

The malaria vaccine made for Hoffman la Roche goes a step beyond genetic engineering. As with the hepatitis B vaccine described earlier, making the vaccine involved identifying an antigen on the parasite's surface which strongly stimulates an immune response; cloning the gene for this antigen and making the antigen in cultures of *E. coli*. But the vaccine makers have gone a step further. They have dissected the large complex protein molecule of the antigen until they have identified the relatively small portion of the molecule which is actually recognized as foreign by the human immune system. This small portion of the molecule is small enough to be synthesized by chemists. Complete proteins are so large and complex that they can only be economically synthesized by enzymes in cell cultures by living organisms. But small pieces of protein molecules, peptides, can be assembled by chemists at reasonable cost. This is how the vaccine made for Hoffman la Roche has been made.

A number of other vaccines, including some to protect animals as well as humans against infectious disease, have been made in the same way. The small immune-stimulating regions of protein antigen from disease organisms have been identified. Only these regions have been synthesized to use in vaccines. Synthetic vaccines like this are much cheaper to make than either cloned vaccines or conventional vaccines made by growing whole disease organisms in culture. And synthetic vaccines can be made and deployed much more quickly; it takes far less time to synthesize large quantities of a chemical than it does to build up cell cultures large enough to clone equivalent quantities. So, while synthetic vaccines could not have been made without first cloning antigens, it looked for a while as if they might supplant cloned vaccines.

However, tests of the synthetic malaria vaccine on human volunteers have shown that it is far from completely successful in giving protection against malaria. Thirty-five volunteers – young healthy medical students – were vaccinated with this synthetic vaccine. Most but not all produced antibodies showing they had at least some degree of immunity to malaria. The three volunteers who had produced the highest levels of antibodies were then deliberately infected with malaria by infected mosquitoes. Only one of the three turned out to be completely protected; he had no parasites in his bloodstream and no symptoms of infection. The other two did show a delay in the appearance of parasites in their bloodstream, compared to others who were infected who had not been vaccinated but later they developed malaria.

Malaria vaccines are now being tested on a large scale, but they are likely to have a long way to go before they are fully effective. As mentioned earlier, there are two reasons for this; the complexity of the parasite's life cycle, and the relative weakness of the immune system's reaction to single antigens. It now seems likely that the reaction to small parts of individual antigens is weaker still. However, the first problem could well be solved in the future by more elaborate genetic engineering. Vaccines will be made which contain cocktails of antigens from all the main stages of the parasite's life cycle; sporozoite, merozoite and gametocyte.

A vaccine or part of a vaccine made to stimulate an immune reaction against the last-named, the gametocyte stage of the life cycle, has been nicknamed the 'Altruistic' vaccine. It will do nothing to help the person it is injected into. But, by destroying the stage of the parasite which lives and reproduces in mosquitoes, it will stop the infection spreading to other people.

The second problem, the weakness of the immune system's reaction to single antigens, will also be solved by making a cocktail vaccine, but a cocktail of a different kind. The relative weakness of the immune response to single antigen vaccines disappointed scientists and doctors. For a while it looked as though the ability to clone antigens to make vaccines might prove far less valuable than had been hoped, because such vaccines would give insufficient protection. But further research has begun to show the way round the problem.

Gene cloning is making it possible to dissect the way in which white cells respond to foreign proteins; antigens, at the molecular level and it is becoming clear that more than one antigen is required

33

so as to stimulate different parts of the immune response. It is also clear that these antigens alone are not enough, they have to be 'seen' – immunologists actually use the word – with other antigens around them, to convince the immune system that something is up.

When a bacterium, for example, is attacked by the immune system, the reaction depends on the bacterium's antigens first being recognized as foreign by one class of white blood cell called T-cells (standing for Thymus Derived cells). These cells somehow learn to distinguish friend from foe, self from non-self, by spending part of their lives in the thymus gland near the heart. Then the T-cells stimulate another class of white cells called B-cells (standing for bone-marrow-derived cells, because they originate in the bone marrow, like all white cells, but unlike T-cells do not migrate to the thymus) to poduce antibodies. The antibodies fasten on to the bacteria and may themselves kill it. Then, together with more chemical agents, these antibodies also label the bacteria as targets for another kind of attack, in which T-cells close in on the bacteria, come into contact with them and destroy them by making holes in the bacterium's protective outer membrane.

Understanding how different antigens stimulate these various arms of the immune response has progressed in parallel with the making of cloned vaccines. Neither would have been possible without genetic engineering. As it became apparent that vaccines made from single antigens are not enough to stimulate strong immunity, so immunologists have begun to discover which extra antigens are needed to stimulate which arms of the immune response. Antigens which stimulate the B-cells' antibody-mediated response, other antigens which stimulate the T-cell's cell-mediated response, and still others which provide the contexts in which the stimulating antigens need to be 'seen', must all be built into cloned or synthetic vaccines.

So, for a cloned vaccine to protect against a typical parasitic disease, it will need antigens from all the stages of the parasite's life cycle, each set being chosen to stimulate both antibody-mediated and cell-mediated immunity, together with antigens to set these first antigens in the proper context to be recognized, as clearly part of a foreign organism. Such vaccines, it is now being predicted, will stimulate immunity as powerfully – or nearly as powerfully – as conventional vaccines made from whole disease organisms. In this way genetic engineers making vaccines have overcome their first, formidable setback. Research using genetic engineering to investigate immunity has shown how to overcome it, using more elaborate genetic engineering.

Another immensely important and unconquered tropical parasitic disease, against which a vaccine cannot be made by conventional techniques, is schistosomiasis, also known as bilharzia. Bilharzia, caused by many-celled parasites, schistosomes, affects not only some 250 million people, mainly in tropical Africa, but also countless cattle and buffalo. It is on the increase in some areas because big irrigation schemes provide new breeding grounds for the fresh-water snails which harbour the larvae of the schistosomes.

As with malaria, many experts agree that a vaccine is necessary for realistic hopes of eradicating schistosomiasis over large areas. Again as with malaria, inability to grow the parasite on a large scale outside the human body made a vaccine an impossibility until gene cloning came along.

There is a special problem in making a vaccine to protect against schistosomes, for they have evolved their own protection against the human immune system. Schistosomes grow into larvae inside fresh-water snails, burst out of the snails and penetrate the skin of anyone standing in the water. When the larvae reach the bloodstream they cover themselves with human – or, if they are species which parasitise animals, animal – protein material. This disguise seems to protect them from being recognized by their hosts' immune system.

But research has shown there is a period, after schistosomes have got into the body and before they cover themselves in human proteins, during which they are vulnerable to recognition and destruction by the immune system. However, killing schistosomes involves no less than four different classes of blood cells. So as to be effective in stimulating protective immunity against schistosomes, a vaccine will have to stimulate all four classes of cells.

This is a tall order, and immunologists are still experimenting with the needed antigens to create the perfect vaccine. But a French research team, led by Professor Andre Capron of Lille University, working for the French national genetic engineering company Transgene, have cloned a vaccine for schistosomiasis. It has been shown to protect a wide range of animals, including monkeys, against subsequent invasion by schistosome larvae. By the time this book is published this vaccine will almost certainly have been tested in humans. The 'cocktail' approach should produce better and better vaccines for schistosomiasis, if resources are made available.

Several common tropical diseases are caused by species of single-celled parasites called trypanosomes, distinguished by whip-like 'tails' called flagellae which they use to swim around. Antigens which stimulate immunity against the trypanosomes which cause two common diseases, Leishmaniasis and Chagas' disease (common in the Middle East and Latin and Central American respectively), have already been identified, by French scientists in the Centre for the Study of Parasite Immunology in Lille University. The next steps will be to clone these antigens, make experimental vaccines and test them in animals and after that in humans.

The toughest challenge for genetic engineers seeking to make vaccines to protect against the tropical parasitic diseases is, undoubtedly, sleeping sickness, trypanosomiasis. The species of 'tryp' which causes sleeping sickness, *Trypanosomas cruzi* has evolved a clever way to evade the immune response; by continually changing its surface antigens. By the time the body of a person invaded by these parasites has mounted an immune response against one set of antigens on the tryp's surface, it will have changed them to another set. Antibodies made against the first set of antigens find nothing to react with. Thus, a vaccine made from one set of antigens from *T. cruzi* will only stimulate antibodies to react with, and white cells to watch out for, those particular antigens. If tryps in the body then replace those antigens with different ones the tryps' presence will pass unnoticed until the immune system has gone through the process of recognizing the new antigens – by which time the tryps will have replaced them with a third lot.

In contrast to the situation with other parasites, up to now genetic engineers have failed to find any way to outwit *T. cruzi*'s evasion of the immune response. Drugs that will strip away the changeable outer coat of the tryp revealing unchanging antigens underneath may be a possibility; drugs that will 'freeze' the outer coat into one set of antigens to give the immune system time to catch up are another. But such developments are in their infancy.

Leprosy is caused by a bacillus called *Mycobacterium leprae*, a simpler organism than a parasite. But *M. leprae* is another organism that has defied vaccination because it could not be grown outside the human body. When scientists in the UK National Institute for Medical Research discovered *M. leprae* could be grown in the footpads of mice, that was a major breakthrough, making it possible for the first time to do research on the bacillus. Later, it was discovered that *M. leprae* will also grow in the bodies of one species of armadillo, the nine-banded armadillo.

M. leprae grown in this animal's body has been made into vaccine which, at the time of writing, is being tested in large-scale clinical trials in Malawi and India. Earlier trials in Venezuela gave promising results. But because of the slow course of the disease, it will be five or six years before it can be known if this vaccine protects against leprosy. If it does there will be an immediate and massive demand for vaccine in Africa and India – a demand which cannot possibly be supplied by vaccine made in armadilloes. Armadillo ranching is already being strained to the limit to provide enough vaccine for the one hundred thousand doses used in the Malawi trial; if the vaccine works then there will be a demand for many millions of doses.

Only genetic engineering can provide the answer. Individual antigens from *M. leprae* which stimulate immunity have been identified and cloned, ready to be tested in an experimental leprosy vaccine. The task of identifying such antigens was specially hard, harder than in hepatitis B for example, because the main way in which the immune system reacts against *M. leprae* is through cell-mediated immunity, i.e. a direct attack by white blood cells – T-cells – rather than by the making of antibodies.

It is relatively easy to identify antigens which stimulate immunity in the form of antibodies. In these cases, antibodies which are present at high levels in people with strong immunity can be identified and the antigens they are made against can be picked out by the antibodies, and cloned to use in vaccine. It is much harder when the main component of immunity is cell-mediated, as in leprosy. However, an international team of doctors, at the University Hospital of Leiden and the Royal Tropical Institute in the Netherlands and the Hammersmith Hospital in London have succeeded in identifying key antigens.

In order to identify the key antigen the team of doctors took living T-cells from people who had been infected with leprosy and had resisted the disease, as shown by their developing the less severe form (tuberculoid rather than lepromatous leprosy). These T-cells were then grown and multiplied in culture, a process known (like the multiplication of genes in culture), as cloning. T-cells were also cloned from people who had been vaccinated against leprosy using the armadillo vaccine. Then the scientists tested both groups of cloned T-cells with a series of different antigens taken from leprosy bacilli, to see which of them the T-cells recognized as foreign and attacked.

Both the T-cells from people who had been vaccinated against leprosy and the T-cells from people who were naturally resistant to leprosy attacked only two antigens out of all the antigens they were exposed to. This showed that these two antigens on *M. leprae* are those by which the human immune system recognizes the bacillus as foreign in order to attack it.

The two antigens involved have been cloned and, by the time this book is published, will probably have been used in experimental vaccines on human volunteers, to see if they stimulate a strong immune response. If this happens and if there are no side-effects, the next step will be to clone the antigens to use in vaccine on a larger scale – in clinical trials. Such a cloned vaccine could conveniently be ready for large-scale production at about the time when the ongoing trials of the armadillo vaccine have shown that it is possible to protect against leprosy with a vaccine, and vaccine made in armadillos is proving inadequate for the task.

Using vaccines rather than drugs in disease-elimination programmes save medical manpower because a single vaccination lasts for several months or even several years. If it were possible to vaccinate against several diseases simultaneously with a single vaccination, this would save even more medical manpower and, again, be of special value in the developing world. This is now becoming possible through the use of more genetic engineering techniques.

Scientists in the New York State Department of Health have made a vaccine which protects simultaneously against three different diseases. Although it works in a rather different way from cloned or synthetic vaccines, it is equally dependent on genetic engineering. In future the technique they and several other teams have developed for making so called 'multivalent' vaccines, may be used to vaccinate against even more diseases with one single 'jab'.

The three-in-one vaccine has as its base the vaccinia or cowpox virus. This virus, which causes the relatively harmless disease cowpox, was used to vaccinate against smallpox until that disease was finally eliminated in the late 1970s, because immunity to cowpox also confers immunity to smallpox. In the new vaccine vaccinia is used not itself as a vaccine but as a carrier of other vaccines. Vaccinia was chosen for this role because it was used for many years in smallpox vaccination programmes, so pharmaceutical companies are accustomed to growing it and doctors are aware of its limited side effects.

Vaccinia was also used because a particle of vaccinia virus contains – by the standards of viruses – an unusually large amount of DNA. This large genome means it is relatively easy to insert other genes in vaccinia without distorting it. Genes taken from three viruses which cause human diseases; herpes, hepatitis B and influenza were isolated, cloned and then inserted into vaccinia virus particles. The virus with the extra genes was grown and multiplied and then injected into rabbits. The rabbit made antibodies against all four viruses, against hepatitis B, herpes and flu as well as vaccinia. (The same test has since been performed accidentally in humans. Vaccinia virus with other disease genes inserted into it was accidentally injected into one of a team of scientists developing vaccinia based hybrid vaccines. His body produced the appropriate antibodies.) This suggests that a multivalent vaccine, as it is being called, really might protect against several diseases at once.

In the vaccinated person's body the vaccinia virus infects cells and, like any virus, takes over genetic control of the cells it infects. The viral genes instruct the cells to make more virus. The extra genes which have been inserted into the viral genome have effectively become part of the virus, so they behave in the same way as the viral genes. The result is that, as well as making vaccinia virus, the infected cells also make hepatitis B, herpes and influenza antigens, following the instructions of the genes for those antigens which were inserted into the virus.

The immune system of the person involved recognizes the viral antigens made in this way in his or her body as foreign and makes antibodies against them. This sets up immunity against herpes, influenza and hepatitis B. This immunity is usefully reinforced because the body is continually restimulated, in effect revaccinated, with all the viral antigens as the vaccinia virus multiplies and produces more of them.

Some scientists believe that the potential advantages of using vaccinia in this way are so great that the majority of vaccinations will eventually be performed using this technique. Others think that the side-effects of vaccinia itself mean that a better way of giving several vaccinations simultaneously needs to be found. One such alternative could be the use of polio virus as the carrier for a multivalent vaccine.

The idea of using polio vaccine as a carrier for other vaccines grew out of research with another aim in view, to make vaccine made from live attenuated polio virus absolutely safe for use in vaccinating against poliomyelitis (infantile paralysis). There are two kinds of polio vaccine. One, made from killed virus, was devised by the

American scientist, Professor Salk. The other, made from attenuated – i.e. weakened but not killed – virus was devised by another US scientist, Professor Sabin.

The live Sabin vaccine has several advantages over the killed Salk vaccine. It is taken orally while the killed vaccine has to be injected. It prevents infected people spreading virus in their excreta, while the killed vaccine still allows this to happen. And the live vaccine is considerably cheaper to produce. But whereas the killed vaccine is absolutely safe., although the live polio vaccine has an excellent safety record by the standards of vaccines generally, there are a handful of people every year (four or five annually in the USA for example), who suffer some degree of paralysis, usually mild, as a result of live vaccination, because the virus has mutated and regained some degree of virulence.

Professor Jeffrey Almond of Reading University, a pioneering genetic engineer, with colleagues in the British Institute for Biological Standards, has used genetic engineering tehniques to make live polio vaccine 100 per cent safe. The same techniques, Jeffrey Almond then realized, might also be used to make the same vaccine into a multivalent vaccine able to protect against several diseases simultaneously.

Live polio vaccine is made not from one but from a mixture of three different strains of polio virus, types 1,2 and 3, because immunity to just one of these viruses does not protect against the other two. There is a minute but still real chance of a fortuitous combination of mutations (small, random changes in DNA) in types 2 or 3 virus rendering the weakened, attenuated viruses able to cause harmful symptoms again. This however is not true of the third strain in the mixture, type 1 polio virus. It is impossible for it to become virulent again.

Jeffrey Almond and his colleagues have used genetic engineering to create hybrid attenuated viruses, with small pieces of genes from types 2 and 3 viruses inserted into the complete genome of type 1 virus, so as to protect against all three viruses without any risk of infection from mutated type 2 or 3 virus. Earlier research had identified antigens on polio viruses which stimulate strong immunity. Further work picked out small regions of these antigens which actually stimulate immunity. The sections of the genes for the antigens which are the blueprints for making just those antigenic regions were then identified. Just these sections of genes were then inserted into the genome of type 1 polio virus, which was then attenuated, weakened in the usual way to make vaccine. Tests in animals showed the hybrid attenuated vaccine made in this way causes the formation of protective antibodies against all three strains of polio virus.

The next step could be human tests and trials. If they show this genetically engineered vaccine to be as effective in protecting against all three polio viruses as the conventional vaccines, it may come into wide use, because it will combine the advantages of today's live and killed vaccines. Like killed vaccine it will be 100 per cent safe to use, and like today's live vaccine, it will be cheaper to make than killed vaccine, because once the genetic engineering has been performed the altered virus can be grown indefinitely like any ordinary virus. It will also be taken orally and will prevent infection being passed on from a vaccinated person, like conventional live vaccine.

Jeffrey Almond saw great potential for this concept beyond polio. He realised that genes from viruses other than different polio viruses might be inserted into type 1 polio virus and that in this way it might be possible to protect against several diseases simultaneously. This would have the advantage, as with the vaccinia virus, of using as a carrier vaccine an organism which pharmaceutical companies are well accustomed to growing.

Now Almond's work is being supported by the Medical Research Council and the World Health Organisation. He has produced constructs (as genetic engineers call re-arranged DNA) of genetically-engineered polio viruses, incorporating antigens taken from hepatitis A, from some of the viruses which cause the common cold, from chlamydia, the organism that causes the common eye disease trachoma, and from the Human Immune Virus, HIV, that causes AIDS.

There is a special reason for trying polio virus as a 'carrier' for vaccines made to protect against the above list of diseases, and perhaps against more than one of them simultaneously. This is that polio virus infection stimulates the formation of antibodies not inside the body, i.e. in the bloodstream, but outside the body, i.e. on to the surfaces of mucous membranes. These include the lining of the gut through which the polio virus invades, the inside of the nose where rhinoviruses causing colds get in, and the sexual organs where chlamydia and HIV enter.

Most viruses, and consequently most vaccines made from them, stimulate the production of antibodies into the bloodstream. Such antibodies cannot hope to bar entry to viruses that enter through mucous membranes. The hope is that hybrid multivalent vaccines, made using polio virus, will cause antibodies to be made against all the antigens incorporated into the polio virus genome. These antibodies, like those made against the polio virus, will be pushed out on to mucous membranes. Such antibodies could form a first line of defence against, for example, HIV threatening entry via the vagina or anus, or rhinoviruses trying to get in through the nose.

A vaccine which could protect against AIDS and the common cold sounds too good to be true. And, as will be explained in the chapter on AIDS, there are reasons why it is specially difficult to devise a vaccine to protect against AIDS. There is also a special problem with the common cold. It can be caused by any one of about one hundred different rhinoviruses, all with different surface antigens, so that immunity against one does not provide immunity against another. However, recent research has shown that all the cold-causing rhinoviruses known do have a few antigens in common. It may be possible to insert just those antigens into polio virus and use them to stimulate resistance to all the rhinoviruses.

HIV infection is mainly passed through the blood stream, but there is some evidence that in heterosexual intercourse infection may occur through mucous membranes in the vagina. A vaccine which stimulates the formation of antibodies against HIV in the blood may be of little value, since once HIV has entered the bloodstream and infected a few T-cells (T-cells are selectively invaded by HIV which is why it steadily destroys immunity, hence the name Acquired Immune Deficiency Syndrome) the virus can spread from cell to cell by causing infected T-cells to fuse with others not yet infected. Virus spreading in this way never comes into contact with the blood and so is unaffected by antibodies in the blood. Anti-HIV antibodies on mucous membranes in the vagina and anus, on the other hand, might protect against HIV infection before the virus got as far as the blood stream.

(The genetic engineering involved in this approach to vaccination is quite elaborate. Each particle of polio virus contains a single strand of RNA. This means its genetic code takes the form, not of the usual double helix of DNA, but of a single strand of the closely-related but slightly-differing chemical substance RNA. If genes made of DNA from other disease organisms are to be incorporated into polio virus to make multivalent vaccines, they must first be translated from DNA to RNA. Enzymes, called reverse transcriptases, which perform such translations are used routinely by genetic engineers.)

A similar technique is being tried as a means of making malaria vaccine more powerfully protective. As mentioned earlier, in order for foreign antigens to stimulate a strong immune response, they have to be 'seen' by the immune system in the context of other, surrounding antigens. Not just one but a number of different antigens have to be included in a vaccine so as to stimulate the different parts of the immune system and to make the vaccine really protective.

With this in mind a team led by Dr Jerald Sadoff of the Walter Reed Army Institute of Medical Research in the USA, a leading centre for research on tropical parasitic diseases, have inserted genes which code for malarial sporozoite antigens into salmonellae – typhoid bacteria. The salmonellae were then grown in culture and attenuated (weakened to make them harmless), just as they are when they are used to make vaccine to protect against typhoid. The salmonellae with sporozoite genes added were injected into mice. When the mice were subsequently infected with live sporozoites, as though they had been bitten by a malarial mosquito, the sporozoites were destroyed by the mouse's immune system. The mice had been vaccinated against malaria.

This suggests that a vaccine made in the same way might protect humans against malaria. If more research confirms Dr Sadoff's theory about this vaccine, it may have big advantages over other vaccines being made to protect against malaria.

The vaccine is thought to work like this: the attenuated salmonellae injected into the body are absorbed by macrophages, a class of white cells forming part of the immune system , which often form the first stage in an immune reaction against a foreign organism. The macrophages literally carry antigens from the foreign organisms they absorb around the body to other cells of the immune system, so as to show them what needs to be attacked. Because the salmonellae contain genes from malaria parasites, they will also contain malarial antigens made by these genes. So the macrophages will present these antigens, too, to the rest of the immune system. So as well as being alerted to attack any salmonellae bacteria which later enter the body, the immune system will be alerted to attack any malarial parasites which are infected by mosquitoes. The sporozoite stages of the parasite's life cycle, injected by the mosquito, will be attacked, because the genes in the salmonellae come from sporozoites.

A vaccine made in this way, using genetic engineering to combine parasites and bacteria, has important potential advantages. Attenuated salmonellae are already used routinely in vaccinating against typhoid, so they pose no new health hazard. Typhoid vaccine can be taken orally, which is always more acceptable because it avoids the discomfort and extra work of injections.

If the vaccine works in humans, salmonellae with added genes may in future be used to protect against other tropical parasitic diseases. Because the salmonellae are absorbed by macrophages, their effect is to stimulate cell-mediated immunity, in which T-cells attack micro-organisms by direct contact. Macrophages stimulate cell-mediated immunity by presenting T-cells with antigens from foreign organisms which the macrophages have absorbed, in this case salmonellae and plasmodia, malarial parasites.

Cell-mediated immunity is specially important in protecting against all parasitic diseases, including schistosomiasis, leishmaniasis and Chagas' disease. It is also specially important in defending against leprosy. It may be the only kind of immune response that works against HIV. Ultimately, immunity against all these conditions might be provided simultaneously, by a vaccine made from salmonellae with genes from more than one disease organism implanted in them – a vaccine taken orally by swallowing a lump of sugar.

Exactly how T-cells kill by direct contact has not been proved although evidence is accumulating that they first bind very tightly to the surface membrane of the target cell and then drill holes in it by releasing proteins called Perforins which – as their name implies – perforate the target cells' membranes with tiny holes. Simply drilling holes in membranes could be enough to kill the target cells because, once a membrane is holed, water is liable to be absorbed until the swollen cell bursts.

T-cells have other weapons in their arsenals, including killer proteins which they secrete in through the holes they have drilled in bacteria or parasites. When these killer proteins are identified, they too may be cloned and used as drugs, applied from outside the body to help to fight disease organisms, if ways of targetting them as effectively as the T-cell does can be found.

Clearly the new ability to identify, isolate and close genes for disease organisms' antigens and to transfer these genes into cell cultures to clone them, will revolutionize vaccine making. Vaccines which for the first time ever can protect against tropical parasitic diseases and vaccines which can protect against several diseases simultaneously are now being made. Genetic engineers are now assembling vaccines from several cloned antigens, each chosen to protect against a different disease or to stimulate a separate part of the immune response.

The degree of sophistication of the 'second generation' genetic engineering deployed in vaccine making is paralleled in other areas; in the elaborate constructs now being made to protect plants against pests and the hybrid genes being constructed to produce 'guided missile' type drugs to attack cancer, for example. Genetic engineers have only just become able to combine genes and other meaningful sequences of DNA from different sources in such purposeful ways. Where it will lead them in, say, fifty years time defies the imagination.

5

GENES FOR AND AGAINST CANCER AND HEART DISEASE

Genetic engineering is allowing vaccines to be developed to protect against surprising and unexpected diseases. Among them, as well as many more infectious diseases, are forms of cancer.

At least one quarter of all cancers are now thought by researchers to be caused by virus infections, not as the sole cause but as essential steps in chains of events which ultimately lead to cancer. If vaccines can be made to protect against the virus infections then, even though the viruses are not the sole causes of the cancers, the chains of events involved could be interrupted so that those vaccinated do not develop cancer.

The link between a virus infection and a cancer has been most clearly established with the Epstein-Barr or EB virus, named after the two scientists who first discovered its role in cancer. EB virus helps to cause cancer of the nasopharynx, the tissue immediately behind the nose. This is extremely common in southern China, where there are up to eighty thousand new cases every year. EB virus also helps to cause Burkitts lymphoma, a cancer of the lymph glands which is the commonest cancer among children in tropical Africa, with up to ten thousand new cases every year.

A team led by Professor Tony Epstein at Bristol University's Medical School has made a vaccine intended to protect against both these cancers. They identified an antigen on EB virus particles which stimulates immunity strongly, then cloned the antigen's gene in *E.*

coli and used it to make the antigen into an experimental vaccine. The Bristol team have shown this vaccine protects monkeys against infection with EB virus.

Recently the gene for this antigen has been inserted into vaccinia virus by a team at Manchester University. A vaccine to protect against EB virus, derived from vaccinia as described earlier, is being prepared for human tests.

Another vaccine for EB virus has been developed by Dr Andy Morgan in the Bristol Medical School. He has used genetic engineering techniques similar to those used with vaccinia virus to insert genes for an EB virus antigen into the virus which causes a harmless form of chicken pox. This virus is already used in a vaccine which protects children against severe forms of chicken pox. Animal tests have shown that the engineered virus stimulates an immune response against EB virus as well as chicken pox virus. A vaccine of this kind, intended to protect against Burkitts lymphoma in Africa and against nasopharyngeal cancer in China, is soon to undergo human trials.

With cancer, as with tropical parasitic diseases, no vaccines could be possible without genetic engineering. Although other factors are needed to cause the cancers, the perceived risk of the viruses involved causing cancer in laboratory workers is too great for a vaccine to be made in the conventional way, that is by growing a complete virus on a large scale and then attenuating or killing it to use in vaccines. But cloning individual antigens, which are harmless on their own but which can stimulate immunity, is a means of making vaccines which bypasses the need to grow whole viruses.

Another form of cancer which is partially caused by virus infection is cervical cancer. The virus involved is almost certainly a papilloma or wart virus, spread from person to person by sexual intercourse. Other factors, possibly including infection with EB virus as well as papilloma virus, are also needed to cause this form of cancer. But, because infection is an essential prerequisite for cells to become malignant, it is likely that preventing infection with papilloma virus will alone be sufficient to prevent cervical cancer. Papilloma virus antigens which might be cloned to use in vaccines to stimulate immunity to the virus are being identified. A major research programme with the target of a vaccine made from such cloned antigens to protect against cervical cancer has recently been launched in the UK.

Like cancer, Lassa fever – named after the village of Lassa in

Nigeria, where it was first identified – is too deadly a disease for even the most dedicated laboratory staff to be exposed to the virus that causes it. Antigen cloning is needed instead to make a protective vaccine. Most cases of the disease have been reported from Nigeria, but there have also been epidemics in Liberia and the disease is thought to be endemic in parts of Sierra Leone, and perhaps elsewhere in West Africa.

The early stages of Lassa fever produce flu-like symptoms but after about ten days violent vomiting, ulcers and convulsions set in. About half the people admitted to hospital with Lassa fever die. There is no cure. A similar virus, 'Mozambique' virus has been used experimentally in an attempt to immunize against Lassa fever, but there is concern that Mozambique virus, even in attenuated form, could itself be dangerous.

The vaccine for Lassa fever made by Doctors Christopher Clegg and Graham Lloyd in the high security lab in the Public Health Laboratory, at Porton Down near Salisbury, is made by genetic engineering. A single gene taken from the Lassa virus was inserted into vaccinia virus which was then used to vaccinate guinea pigs. They were found to be well protected against subsequent infection. So Lassa fever may join the list of infections which might all be protected against by a single 'shot' of vaccinia engineered with genes from several disease organisms.

There is, however, a problem with the use of vaccinia as a carrier for antigens used to vaccinate against other infections. While vaccinia is relatively harmless to healthy, well-nourished people, infection with it can be unpleasant and even dangerous to people with lowered resistance. But such people will be among those most in need of the multivalent vaccines which scientists hope to build into vaccinia. A research team led by Dr Charles Flexner in the Laboratory for Viral disease in the American National Institute for Allergy and Infectious Diseases is using second or even third generation genetic engineering to try to overcome this problem. His experiments depend not only on the ability to insert genes into vaccinia but also upon new knowledge of the functions of lymphokines.

Charles Flexner and his colleagues have inserted the gene for Interleukin 2 into vaccinia. Interleukin 2 is a chemical messenger, a lymphokine which naturally stimulates immune reactions against micro-organisms generally. When vaccinia virus containing Interleukin 2 genes was used to infect mice, tests showed the added genes made the mice produce extra Interleukin 2. This then protected the mice against any harmful effects due to vaccinia. Interleukin 2 genes could do the same for people vaccinated with vaccinia.

The plan now is to put genes for Interleukin 2 as well as genes for antigens taken from various tropical diseases into vaccinia virus and then, after safety tests, to use it to vaccinate people. The hope is that the genes for the disease organisms will stimulate immunity against the diseases, while the Interleukin 2 gene will prevent any harmful effects of vaccinia. It is also hoped that the Interleukin 2 gene, by making the vaccinated person's body make more of this substance which stimulates immunity, will make their immune system respond more strongly to the vaccine and so strengthen immunity.

More animal research will be needed before the idea can be tried in humans. But it shows how different areas of gene cloning can now be combined to produce formidable new combinations.

Another example of how genetic engineering may allow protection against diseases not thought of as infectious, is in rheumatoid arthritis. The symptoms of rheumatoid arthritis are caused by an auto-immune reaction, that is by the immune system of the affected person attacking and damaging part of his own body. In rheumatoid arthritis the cartilage covering the ends of bones in joints is under attack. Researchers at the Royal Devon and Exeter Hospital have shown that some people infected with a particular virus, of the class known as parvoviruses, develop pain, inflammation and swelling of their joints. More research showed that a small but significant proportion of patients with rheumatoid arthritis are infected with parvovirus.

The conclusion that Dr Valerie Jones of the Devon and Exeter Hospital draws from this is that parvovirus is one of a number of factors which can trigger off rheumatoid arthritis (RA) symptoms in people who are genetically susceptible. The virus has no such effect in people who are not genetically susceptible.

Working with Exeter University scientist Professor John Bryant, Dr Jones has already identified one gene which may be responsible for causing susceptibility to RA. Other genes are also under suspicion. This work should eventually make it possible to identify some people who are at special risk of RA by means of simple blood tests. Such people might then be vaccinated with a vaccine made from parvovirus, to protect them against infections which could otherwise trigger RA. Yet again, such a vaccine could only be made by genetic engineering, because parvoviruses cannot be grown outside the human body. But it should be possible to clone immunity-stimulating antigens from the virus, and to use cloned antigen to make the vaccine.

What is probably happening in the bodies of people affected by parvovirus causing RA symptoms is that their immune systems, in reacting against the virus, also react against a human body protein in the tissue of their joints. This, by an unfortunate coincidence, happens to be identical to a viral antigen, or at least sufficiently similar to it to be attacked by the same immune response.

In normal people this harmful cross-reaction is suppressed before it can do any harm, by the watchdogs for auto-immune reactions, the 'suppressor cells', described earlier. The fact that some people infected with parvovirus begin to develop arthritis-like symptoms, which then subside before causing serious illness, suggests there is a pattern of cross-reaction followed by suppression. A genetic factor – it is going too far to call it a defect – is responsible for the inability of the immune systems of people prone to RA to suppress the harmful auto-immune cross-reaction when it begins to affect human joint tissue.

Although parvovirus is only responsible for RA in a small proportion of those who suffer it, it may provide all-important clues to how RA is caused in other people. Suppose the symptoms are indeed triggered by an immune reaction against a viral antigen which happens to be identical to a joint tissue protein. If other viruses possess the same protein, or even just bits of it which are big enough to stimulate an immune reaction, then infection with those viruses too could cause RA symptoms in people with a defect in their immune systems. Such people lack the watchdogs which normally prevent such a harmful auto-immune reaction.

Bacteria as well as viruses can cause harmful auto-immune reactions and RA. Dr Irun Cohen of the Weizmann Institute of Science in Israel, whose work on multiple sclerosis has already been described, has shown that the cells of the immune system which attack cartilage in auto-immune reactions causing RA symptoms also attack the bacteria which cause TB, Mycobacteria tuberculosis, (M.TB) without needing to be alerted and stimulated as white cells normally do before attacking an enemy they are 'seeing' for the first time. White cells which have learnt to attack cartilage then also know how to attack M.TB. This made Cohen think that a protein or part of a protein in cartilage must be identical to a protein in M.TB and this proved to be the case.

Irun Cohen tracked down the part of a protein which is identical in cartilage and in M. TB. Then he synthesized this chemical, a peptide, on its own, and injected it into rats. Then he attempted to induce arthritis in the rats by injecting them with M.TB. Normally this injection caused RA symptoms in the rats, because their immune systems' reaction against M.TB also damages the cartilage in their joints, because M.TB and cartilage contain the same peptide. But this didn't happen in the rats which had first been injected with the peptide itself.

This was strange. Here is a chemical substance which, when it forms part of a bacterium, is recognized as foreign and stimulates an immune response. The immune system which has been made to react in this way attacks the same substance which, by an unfortunate coincidence, forms part of the cartilage in joints. That's all logical enough. But when the same substance is injected into rats on its own, and they are then infected with M.TB, their immune system does not go on to attack the cartilage. On the face of it, since the immune system has been stimulated twice with the peptide, it might be expected to attack the same peptide in cartilage twice as hard. Instead, it doesn't attack it at all.

The reason, Dr Cohen thinks, is that when the immune system is stimulated by M.TB in an infection, it sees the substance that does the stimulating in the context of the whole bacterium. In the cartilage, the immune system sees the substance in the context of the whole cartilage. This looks enough like bacterium to stimulate the same immune reaction. But when the substance appears out of context, on its own, the immune system sees it as something different, and so suppresses the reaction against it.

That's only the beginning of an explanation. But it also gives clues as to how the whole process of recognizing foreign antigens may work. More important for arthritis sufferers, it may provide a treatment for rheumatoid arthritis. Might injections of the key peptide into humans prone to rheumatoid arthritis protect against it? If such people were subsequently infected with parvovirus, M.TB or anything else containing the fateful peptide, then they might be protected against the harmful auto-immune reaction. In Dr Cohen's own slightly more scientific words, 'The purified peptide [chemical] containing the epitope [the substance in question] might induce therapeutic suppression of the disease process in humans as it does in rats.'

The very latest type of vaccine being developed will it's hoped be able to protect against chemicals in the environment in the same way as people are now protected against infectious diseases.

What Doctors Lawrence Silbart and David Kenn of the Pathology Department of the University of Michigan have done, is to find a way of making the immune system identify and destroy toxic chemical wastes as well as micro-organisms.

The immune system has evolved to protect us against bacteria and viruses. Their surfaces are made of proteins, chemicals with large complex molecules. So the immune system has become very clever at telling the difference between the proteins of the human body it belongs to and defends, and any foreign proteins belonging to micro-organisms that get into the body. But because there were no industrial waste products around while the immune system was evolving, it can't identify the much smaller and simpler molecules of toxic waste products as being foreign. So they often get into the body and do damage without being neutralized and eliminated.

Silbart and Keen have got round this limitation by adding a man-made toxic chemical to a protein from a bacterium so that, as the immune system learns to recognize and attack the one, it also learns to recognize and attack the other. This makes it possible to vaccinate to protect against the toxic chemical at the same time as the disease caused by the bacterium. A vaccine consists of dead bacteria, or viruses or parasites, or just anitgens from them, which can be recognized as foreign, which stimulate the immune system when they get into the human body, but don't cause disease. If a real infection follows later then the immune system of the vaccinated person doesn't have to waste time learning to recognize the infection as foreign but recognizes it and attacks it straightaway. This usually provides complete protection against the disease.

What Silbart and Keen did was to couple an industrial chemical which causes cancer, actylaminofluorine (AAF) to the toxin produced by cholera bacteria and use this hybrid material, a conjugate as it's called, as a vaccine. When they injected it into rabbits they found the rabbits made antibodies against AAF as well as against cholera. The antibodies were produced on the mucus-covered membrane lining the intestine where food is absorbed into the body, because cholera bacteria get in through the intestine. Tests showed that these anti-bodies against AAF, while they didn't stop it all getting into the body, did reduce the amount that got in by more than half. By refining the technique and coupling cholera toxin to other industrial toxic wastes in vaccines, it should be possible to give some degree of protection to humans who have to work in chemically hazardous environments.

The antibodies will probably also be produced into other mucus membranes in the body, such as those of the nose and the sexual organs. This sort of vaccine might in the future be developed to protect us against toxic chemicals we are liable to absorb from the air we breathe as well as those we swallow. And they might be combined with vaccines to protect us against sexually transmitted disease. As you've read, it is now possible to make vaccines able to protect against several different diseases simultaneously, using genetic engineering. Now it may also become possible to make such vaccines also protect us against some toxic chemicals in the environment.

So, genetic engineering and allied techniques are beginning to show how we may become able to protect against some of the hazards of the rich world; cancer, rheumatoid arthritis and toxic chemicals. The same is true of coronary heart disease, CHD.

CHD, in which damage to heart muscle is caused by interruption to its blood supply via the coronary arteries, is the leading cause of death among men in Western countries. Deaths from CHD are now declining in the USA and Australia, thanks to enlightened public opinion, but they are stationary in the UK and most of Western Europe, and on the increase in urban areas in some developing countries and parts of Eastern Europe.

The immediate cause of CHD is thrombosis, the formation of blood clots in coronary arteries superimposed on atherosclerosis, hardening and thickening of arterial walls and consequent narrowing of arteries. The environmental factors that contribute to CHD are well established; smoking, obesity, high consumption of animal fats and high blood pressure. (There is conflicting evidence about the part played by personality. Some studies suggest that the aggressive competitive, insecure Type A person is at higher risk than the relaxed Type B, but other studies disagree – partly through difficulty in defining such personalities with the precision needed to produce meaningful statistics.)

But it is also clear that family background and in particular whether or not close relatives, especially male relatives, have suffered CHD is also very important in determining susceptibility. Clearly genetic factors are important. The inherited genes that predispose to CHD are rightly called genetic variations or factors rather than defects or abnormalities, because they are so common. Their high frequency in populations today demonstrates that prehistoric man's life was too nasty, brutish and short for the genes that predispose to CHD in modern life to have had much, if any, influence on natural selection.

Humans, creatures who evolved over millions of years to survive and succeed in living an active, often hectic and dangerous life, eating a mixed, largely vegetarian, often sparse diet, have over a few thousand years at most completely changed their way of life. This is especially true of those in urban areas in developing as well as developed countries. Diets high in animal fats, little exercise, obesity and smoking have become very common. They are all factors predisposing to heart disease.

Today these environmental factors often work together with genetic factors that also predispose to heart disease. A few thousand years ago, the genetic factors were unimportant because life was short. Someone whose genes predisposed him to hardening of the arteries in his forties would have been unlikely to live that long. And in a short life, with a sparse diet and a lot of exercise, genes which today are disadvantageous might actually have been beneficial. Genes which predispose men to keep high levels of cholesterol circulating in the blood, for example, are harmful in a sedentary life because the cholesterol is kept hanging about and gets laid down on the walls of arteries. But in prehistory, such genes may have been valuable, by providing a high-quality energy reserve in the form of blood cholesterol, ready for instant and frequent use.

What this means is that modern man has a startlingly high incidence of genetic variations which, in reasonably well-off urban conditions today are very likely to lead to heart attacks, and that evolution is much too slow a process to have begun to get rid of such now-harmful genes by natural selection. Genetic engineering cannot cure heart attacks, nor is it any substitute for sensible healthy diet, reasonable exercise, giving up smoking and losing excessive weight. Anyone can take such measures to give his or her body and especially his or her heart a healthier way of life.

But what genetic engineering can do and is doing is to reveal just how our genes make so many of us specially vulnerable to CHD. With that knowledge we are acquiring the ability to identify people who are at special risk of coronary thrombosis, so as to warn them to do everything possible to avoid a lifestyle which encourages thrombosis and to live a healthy lifestyle. Beyond that, those at risk can be given precautionary therapy, perhaps an aspirin a day to discourage blood clotting, perhaps more extreme measures for those at higher risk.

We now know a lot about the genetic factors that predispose to coronary heart disease. The techniques which now allow scientists to identify, isolate, multiply and analyse individual genes and their products, the proteins the genes code for, have made possible, in just the last few years, the first real, detailed understanding of atheros-clerosis and harmful blood clotting. The way in which fats are transported in the bloodstream, and how they are taken out of it through the walls of arteries, is also increasingly understood. It has become clear that several different genes are involved in controlling these processes, and that variations in any of these genes can strongly affect an individual's susceptibility to CHD. The more such variations he or she has, the greater his or her risk of heart disease.

In the Bernard Sunley research laboratory near the new Charing Cross Hospital in Fulham, South-West London, a team of twenty scientists led by Dr Steven Humphries, a leading researcher on the genes that predispose to heart disease, are tracking down those genes and the genetic variations that cause the problems.

One set of genes controls the transport of fats including cholesterol out of the blood. These genes make the proteins which have to combine with fats before the fats can be taken out of the blood-stream. Only when they are attached to protein molecules of just the right shapes and sizes can fat molecules be transported out of arteries through receptors, minute holes specially shaped to allow the pro-teins and fats to escape through the walls of arteries.

It is not just a matter of the receptors being the right shape and size to allow the protein-and-fat combine through. The protein has to react with the receptor like a key unlocking a lock; both 'key' and 'lock' have to be the right shapes otherwise the protein won't go through. So a slight variation in the gene for the protein which carries fats out of arteries will alter the shape of the 'key' and slow up or even stop the fat getting out. So will a slight variation in the structure of the gene for the receptor itself, the 'lock'.

So you might expect, what is indeed the case, that the genes for both the carrier proteins and the fat receptors have variants which are now known to be linked to a higher-than-normal incidence of heart disease, because they cause higher-than-normal levels of fat in the bloodstream, so there is a greater chance of some of it coming out of blood into fatty deposits on the walls of arteries.

In the fact the story is already known to be more complicated than that. The single most important gene involved in heart disease is called Apolipoprotein A 1 (Apo A 1). Apo A 1 is the blueprint for making the protein part of High Density Lipoprotein (HDL). Lipopro-tein is what is formed when fats combine with proteins. It is High Density Lipoprotein, HDL which is the form in which fats are transported out of arteries through the receptors on the arterial wall. High levels of HDLs in the blood are good, not bad, because they mean that fat in the blood is being combined into a form in which it can be removed from the bloodstream. So it's not surprising that men who have had coronary heart attacks are much more likely than men who have not to have variations in their Apo A 1 genes.

HDLs are good for us. But there is another form of fat-and-protein combine, called Low Density Lipoprotein, LDL, which is the villain of the fatty scene. LDLs, like HDLs, can be removed from arteries through receptors in the artery walls. But when LDLs accumulate to high levels this removal doesn't happen fast enough. Then fats from LDLs are laid down as solid deposits on artery walls. Variations in the genes which code for LDLs, or for the receptors through which they vanish from the bloodstream, will tend to slow removal and so are always bad news.

Several other genes which affect liability to CHD have been pinpointed. There is the gene for an enzyme which breaks down fats in the bloodstream – another important way in which they are got rid of. If that gene is deficient, up go levels of LDLs and up goes the risk of narrowed, blocked arteries. Then there is the blood clotting mechanism. Normally blood clots only when we are wounded, as a first stage in wound healing. The first stage in blood clotting involves a blood protein called fibrinogen breaking up into smaller molecules called fibrin. If there is too much fibrinogen in the blood, then it will be too easy to trigger the break up into fibrin and for clots to start to form. The clotting mechanisms will be a bit trigger-happy, with added risk of blocked arteries. There is now a gene known with a variant with just this effect.

Macrophages, those invaluable multi-purpose scavengers crop up again and again in immunology, always doing the dirty jobs, always carrying out some thankless but vital task. They are to be found in the walls of arteries in the liver, where they suck cholesterol out of the passing blood. In the process the macrophages become so stuffed with cholesterol that they acquire a foamy look and have actually been christened foam cells. Yet another gene involved in liability to CHD is the one which is responsible for an enzyme which removes cholesterol from overstuffed macrophages. A defect in this gene leads to the macrophages becoming so over stuffed with cholesterol that they themselves become part of the thickening of arterial walls.

The process of identifying such genes and their variant forms which can make us susceptible to CHD is a remorseless process. The gene-hunting techniques are so predictable that it is possible for Dr

Humphries to say, with a fair degree of certainty, that all the genes involved and their variants that cause problems will be known in molecular detail in perhaps five, certainly in ten years time. Humphries and his colleagues are now constructing libraries of gene probes which will be used to establish infallibly which and how many of such variants someone possesses.

Then it will be possible to use routine tests to provide someone with a personal genetic health profile, showing their precise risk of heart disease. As time goes on, genetic profiles for susceptibilities to more and more diseases – cancers, arthritis, mental illnesses, senile dementia and more – will be possible.

6

ENGINEERING A NEW GENERATION OF ANTIBIOTICS

Antibiotics were discovered and developed before scientists knew that genes were made of DNA. The consequence has been that the search for new antibiotics and the improvement of old ones has been an empirical business. Industrial microbiologists have been quite successful in raising the yield of antibiotics – producing micro-organisms, by an endless search for novel organisms, moulds and streptomycetes and by mutating – deliberate but random altering of the moulds' genes in the hope that a tiny proportion of such changes would result in improved antibiotics. But research into the genetics of antibiotic-producing organisms, with the aim of discovering exactly how antibiotic production is controlled, has lagged behind. Now a second generation of genetically-engineered antibiotics is on the way.

At the John Innes Agricultural Research Institute near Norwich, Professor David Hopwood is using gene splicing techniques to improve on natural antibiotics and the organisms that produce them. Hopwood aims both to raise the yield of existing antibiotics and to produce completely new ones. 'Traditionally', says Hopwood, 'yield improvement has been done by a very hit-and-miss process of random mutation and screening for improvements and more mutation and more screening. It's a very hit-and-miss operation and very time-consuming.'

One of David Hopwood's targets is to shift genes for part of one antibiotic from one organism, a streptomycete (streps) that makes an antibiotic into another, thus creating hybrid antibiotics with advantages over both the antibiotics originally made by the two streptomycetes involved. In 1984 his team produced the world's first hybrid antibiotic. Working with Spanish geneticist Dr Paco Maplatido, David Hopwood's team took genes from one species of streptomycete and transplanted them into another species which also produced an antibiotic. The two species did not mate and exchange genes naturally; genetic engineering was needed to move genes from one into the other. The outcome was a new hybrid streptomycete which would never exist in nature. It produces an antibiotic which is a chemical hybrid of and has some of the properties of each of the two antibiotics made by the two streptomycetes from which the hybrid was made.

Professor Hopwood has christened the hybrid antibiotic Mederhodin, because it is a cross between medermycin and actinorhodin, the two antibiotics made by the two species whose genes were, in Hopwood's own phrase, 'scrambled' to make Mederhodin. Mederhodin has no medical value, making it was what scientists call a model system, a way of showing something can be done. It was chosen because its two parent antibiotics have distinctive colours, so it was easy to see when the hybrid streptomycete was producing a hybrid antibiotic because its colour is half-way between the colours of the original two antibiotics.

David Hopwood's success in making Mederhodin opens the way to making a host of other hybrid antibiotics, for many other purposes besides combatting bacterial infections. His hybrid is made from streptomycetes, soil bacteria, which although less well known to the public than moulds like pencillium, in fact make up the majority of antibiotics used today. Seventy of today's commercially-important antibiotics are made by streps, compared to only four made by moulds such as penicillium (though those made by moulds include the penicillins and cephalosporins).

As well as being used in medicine against bacteria, antibiotics made by streps are used to attack fungal pests of crops (for example kasugamycin used against rice blast disease in Japan); to kill nematode worm pests in the soil; to help cows digest their food more efficiently and as anti-cancer agents.

Professor Hopwood is working with collaborators in Ohio State University and Kitasato University in Tokyo, to scramble genes purposefully to make hybrid antibiotics for a host of purposes.

Anti-cancer drugs with fewer side effects on normal healthy tissue are one target. Antibiotics to use against human and plant fungal diseases are another. There is also the continuing need to devise antibiotics to combat bacteria which have become resistant to existing antibiotics, which are a major problem in some hospitals.

Making new antibiotics is only one aim of research into streptomycete and fungal genetics. Another target is to raise their productivity. Genetic engineering makes it potentially possible to pack antibiotic-producing organisms with extra genes for antibiotic production, with little extra sequences called promoters added to drive the streptomycetes to work much harder than normal to make the products of the genes.

An example is ongoing work to use genetic engineering to produce strains of streps which would make rifampicin, an antibiotic used to treat leprosy and TB, much more prolifically than the streps used to make rifampicin today. This would make the antibiotic cheaper and so more widely available in the developing world where it is most needed.

David Hopwood, who is probably the world's leading expert on streptomycete genetics, comes back repeatedly to the need for fundamental research to understand why – as well as how – streps make antibiotics, if their full potential is to be exploited. In making and manipulating lymphokines and antibodies, scientists are drawing on and improving on the human body's biochemical resources. Clearly there are many more resources to be exploited in the human body. But they are much better understood than the resources of other species. 'Antibiotics', says Hopwood, 'are only a fraction, perhaps a small fraction, of the interesting small molecules that streptomycetes make. Compounds which kill parasitic worms, and potentially biodegradable herbicides, are among the other molecules.'

Another possibility is to use streptomycetes as cloning organisms for human and other genes and their products, such as the lymphokines discussed earlier. Streps are organisms which pharmaceutical companies already know how to grow in huge quantities to make antibiotics. Now the genetic manipulation techniques needed to insert human genes into streps have to be developed.

There are good reasons to invest more in fundamental research on the control of metabolism in moulds and streptomycetes. Through the Biotechnology Directorate of the Science and Engineering Research Council and four pharmaceutical companies;

Beecham, Glaxo, Apecel and ICI, the Government are jointly funding a major research programme at eleven British universities and polytechnics with the aim of discovering more about the genetic control of antibiotic production.

Just one example of the work in this programme is the breakthrough recently made by Dr David Hodgson of Warwick University, who has discovered a substance made by streptomycetes which will stimulate mutant streps which never normally make antibiotics do so. Dr Hodgson is now cloning the gene for this substance. It or its gene could be used to stimulate antibiotic production in bioreactors to order.

When streps stop growing and start to make antibiotics – the two changes always go together – some biochemical reactions inside them are stepped up a thousand fold. 'When growth ceases antibiotic production becomes the motorway of the biochemical pathways in streps,' says Dr Iain Hunter, Manager of the Antibiotic and Recombinant DNA Programme. 'We are looking for ways not only to switch traffic onto this motorway, but to keep traffic moving and to add extra lanes to the motorway, by adding extra genes to streps and moulds.'

7

AIDS: HOPES REST IN GENETIC ENGINEERING

AIDS; Acquired Immune Deficiency Syndrome, is caused by the infection of white blood cells, part of the immune system, with HIV, the Human Immune Virus. HIV particles infect only one class of white cells, the so-called T-helper cells, but these T-cells normally play a specially important role in identifying and attacking viruses and other disease organisms that enter the body. As the virus spreads from T-cell to T-cell, rendering the infected cells unable to recognize and destroy other viruses, it progressively weakens the ability of the immune system of the infected person to recognize and destroy other viruses and other 'germs'. In this way immunity is progressively weakened until eventually the infected person dies, often of an infection or a cancer which the immune system of a normal, healthy person would have fought off with ease.

HIV is one of a class of viruses called retroviruses which naturally integrate their own viral genes in among the genes in the nuclei of the cells they infect. Genes from retroviruses become virtually part of the infected cell except at times when they replicate. Then the viral genes cause copies of themselves – messengers – to be made just as the cell's own genes do. These travel out in the usual way to the ribosomes, where messengers are transcribed into new viral proteins, which are made into new virus particles, which then go on to infect more cells.

New understanding of immunity and how viruses bypass it has revealed just how formidable an antagonist HIV is. So formidable, that despite the billions of pounds being spent on AIDS research no one has yet come up either with a drug able to do more than slow up the progress of the disease or with a vaccine able to protect against it. But molecular biology and genetic engineering are now making it possible to devise logical strategies to play the virus at its own game and try to outwit it. Twenty, even ten years ago before the age of genetic engineering the AIDS plague would have left the human race wholly at a loss. As it is genetic engineering offers strong hopes of developing drugs within a few years that will at least allow an AIDS patient to live with his virus like a diabetic with diabetes.

Effective protective vaccines may lie further in the future. But eventually the weight of ingenuity now being focussed on vaccine development seems bound to crack formidable problems in the way. Last to come will be a cure. An agent that can recognize the presence of latent retroviral genes buried deep in cells and destroy them is still far away.

Realistic hopes of making vaccines to protect against AIDS rests with genetic engineering because, as with some other viruses described earlier, HIV is so infallibly deadly that it could never be grown on the huge scale required to make vaccine in the conventional way – from killed or weakened virus taken from large-scale cell cultures. HIV is cultured only in the world's few true high-security labs, where special precautions are observed to prevent its escape; special containment cabinets, protective clothing and negative air pressure in the lab. Such precautions are found only in the USA, USSR, UK, France and West Germany.

As with other specially deadly viruses, genetic engineering offers an alternative route for vaccine making. Genes for antigenic (immunity-stimulating) proteins in HIV particles are identified, after which just those genes are transferred into laboratory cell cultures, which then produce the single, harmless, viral antigen according to the instructions of the inserted gene.

The American genetic engineering company MicroGeneSys has made and tested such a vaccine, which is now undergoing clinical trials. The vaccine was produced from an HIV gene isolated by the US National Institute of Allergy and Infectious Diseases (NIAID). MicroGeneSys used insect virus (baculovirus grown in caterpillars) with the HIV gene inserted into it to make large quantities of the antigen. (The antigen used is not the protein which forms the coat of HIV particles, which is known as gp120, but a somewhat different protein which is formed earlier and then transformed into gp120. It is called gp160. Animal tests showed, surprisingly, that gp160 stimulates a more powerful immune response than gp120).

This vaccine is being tested in high risk groups; drug users who share needles and promiscuous homosexuals. The numbers of those who are vaccinated who later develop AIDS symptoms will be compared with the numbers of equivalent controls with similar lifestyles who have not been vaccinated. Tests in chimpanzees have shown the vaccine caused the production of good levels of circulating antibodies and was also effective in stimulating cell-mediated immunity, that is activity by T-cells which can attack virus-infected cells and destroy the virus in them as well as the cell.

These are quite hopeful signs, but there are several special problems to be overcome in developing an AIDS vaccine. One is that It will take several years to discover how effective vaccination is, because the symptoms of AIDS take an average nine years to develop after infection. It has been suggested that researchers might vaccinate themselves and then expose themselves deliberately to infection, to speed up evaluation of a vaccine. But as knowledge of HIV has grown so it has become increasingly clear that to do so would be foolhardy in view of how little is really known as to how protective a vaccine may be against HIV. No one has devised a vaccine to protect against any retrovirus, nor against any virus that infects cells of the immune system until now, and there are likely to be side-effects that only human tests will reveal.

A further problem is that even if a vaccine made from one coat protein is effective in protecting against some strains of HIV, it may not be effective against others. This is because coat proteins vary in detailed structure between different strains of HIV, of which there are now known to be several. An immune system stimulated to recognize one strain may not recognize another. Whether differing strains will be recognized and how strongly they will be recognized and attacked depends on how big the differences are and if they occur in a part of a coat protein which is particularly important in recognition. Gp160 was chosen because, being the precursor from which coat proteins are made, it varies less between different strains of virus than does the finished coat protein itself, gp120. Vaccines made from gp120 are now however also under test or development.

Other vaccines are being developed for AIDS using more elaborate and sophisticated variants of genetic engineering. Among them are vaccines based on vaccinia virus. As described in an earlier chapter, genes from other disease organisms can be inserted into vaccinia, the relatively harmless cowpox virus. If such an engineered virus is used to vaccinate people then, as well as stimulating an immune response against cowpox, the disease caused by vaccinia, the vaccination will also stimulate immune responses against the organisms from which genes were taken and added to vaccinia. At least one vaccine made by inserting an HIV gene into vaccinia(, the gene for gp160,) is now being tested by the pharmaceutical company Bristol-Myers at the University of Washington in Seattle.

Another ingenious approach to an AIDS vaccine comes from a husband-and-wife team, Doctors Sue and Alan Kingsman of the Oxford Department of Biochemistry and the genetic engineering company British Biotechnology. The Kingsmans have been study-ing yeast transposons, particles of DNA found in yeasts which behave almost but not quite like viruses. Transposons can help to answer fascinating questions of pure science, such as; did viruses evolve from bits of DNA that naturally move around inside cells, are they bits of DNA that have escaped from the control of cells, or did the opposite happen? Did viruses evolve separately and then move into cells, so effectively that some of them have actually become parts of the cells they once invaded? Or have both processes gone on in parallel?

Along the way medical potential for the yeast transposons surfaced. Analysis showed that the particles, known as Ty parti-cles, standing for Transposon yeast, very closely resemble retrovir-uses such as HIV. This may explain how retroviruses evolved – they may be escaped transposons – but it also suggests how an AIDS vaccine may be made.

Ty particles consist of a core of DNA surrounded by a coat made of a single protein. The structure is so virus-like that Ty particles have been nicknamed pseudoviruses. The Kingsmans have shown that it is possible to insert other genes into Ty particles and that, when this is done, the proteins which the genes code for are produced into the coat of the particles, interspersed with the particles' own coat protein.

This suggested another way to try to make a vaccine to protect against AIDS. Experience with vaccines made from single cloned antigens to protect against other diseases shows one antigen on its own does not stimulate immunity nearly as strongly as an old-fashioned vaccine made from complete killed virus particles. The immune system of the vaccinated person has, as immunologists say, to 'see' the antigen that stimulates immunity in the context of some at least of the rest of the virus particle around it, in order for immunity to be properly stimulated. But the deadly HIV cannot be grown in culture to make vaccine from whole virus particles.

The pseudovirus particles suggested an alternative to the Kingsmans. Why not insert a single gene taken from HIV, perhaps the gene for the gp160 protein, into Ty particles? Then the gene would be expressed on the surfaces of the particles. That is, they would carry gp160 on their surfaces, dotted around among the Ty particles' own surface protein. If such particles were used in a vaccine, then they would present gp160 antigens to the vaccinated person's immune system in a context very like that of a real HIV virus particle; the same shape and size, but harmless because it would carry just one HIV gene and one HIV antigen.

This construct – as such DNA hybrids are called – is now being tested in animals and if it looks good will soon be tested in humans. A major problem with testing vaccines against AIDS is that HIV doesn't affect animals in the same way as humans. So for the first test of their idea the Kingsmans are making pseudovirus-type vaccines to protect against animal diseases caused by viruses similar to HIV; a form of leukaemia in cats and a disease similar to AIDS in chimpanzees. Genes from the retroviruses which cause these diseases are being taken and put into pseudoviruses and the pseudoviruses are being used to vaccinate cats and chimps. These are then tested with the real viruses to see if they are protected against the diseases. If cats and chimps can be protected, then the next step will be human tests of a pseudovirus with the gp160 gene in it, first just to see if it causes a good immune response, then for real to try to protect high risk groups against HIV.

At British Biotechnology the Kingsmans and others are digging into the AIDS virus structure, trying different antigens as possible candidates for inserting into pseudovirus particles. HIV has evolved to evade immunity by keeping any proteins which might stimulate a strong response well hidden. It may be possible to identify such proteins and build them in the surfaces of pseudovirus particles, to produce imitation HIV particles which stimulate immunity much more strongly than the real thing.

The value of the pseudovirus may extend far beyond AIDS. It should be possible to introduce genes taken from several different infective organisms into one pseudoviral particle, and to use such engineered particles to vaccinate against several diseases with one 'jab'. Hopefully this would provide immune protection against all the diseases, because the pseudovirus would mimic the sort of way in which the natural viruses present antigens to the immune system.

It may also be possible to identify antigens, perhaps taken from other viruses, which stimulate different arms of the immune response strongly. One antigen from Hepatitis B virus seems to stimulate cell-mediated immunity against all infective organisms. By identifying such antigens and assembling a cocktail of their genes, it may be possible to create pseudoviruses which stimulate immunity against all kinds of infection much more strongly even than vaccines made from entire disease organisms, as well as creating pseudoviruses which can protect powerfully against several infectious diseases simultaneously.

Vaccinia is not the only virus which could be used as a carrier for AIDS antigens in a vaccine. Another candidate which could have advantages is the polio virus. Professor Jeffrey Almond at Reading University has shown that genes from other disease organisms can be inserted into the polio virus before it is killed or inactivated to use as a vaccine and that, as with vaccinia, immunity against the organisms the genes were taken from is stimulated when the altered virus is used as a vaccine.

The Polio virus stimulates the production of antibodies not in the blood but out onto the surface of the mucous membranes of the body, in the nose, sexual organs and lining of the gut. Professor Almond thinks that attenuated polio vaccine with added HIV genes should cause defensive antibodies to be pushed out on to the surface of the lining of the vagina, and anus. The hope is that this could protect against the virus ever gaining entry to the body via the bloodstream, through the most usual ports of entry.

Once HIV is in the bloodstream, then it is very hard to stop its spread from T-cell to T-cell, since it is able to spread by making infected cells fuse with other cells, without virus particles having to emerge into the bloodstream and expose themselves to the immune system to be recognized and attacked. There's a lot to be said for a vaccine that might stop HIV ever getting into the body. It may seem a forlorn hope, but in fact evidence from other diseases – gut infections which are guarded against by antibodies on mucous membranes – suggests that such protection can be surprisingly effective.

With the polio virus as with vaccinia and pseudovirus, there is the hope that it may be possible to insert genes from more than one infective organism and so to protect against several diseases with one vaccination. Using polio vaccine, such diseases would be chosen because the viruses or other organisms which cause them gain access to the body through mucous membranes. So the illnesses which might be protected against by a carrier vaccine based on the polio virus include; the eye disease trachoma which is spread sexually, the papilloma viruses now thought probably to cause cervical cancer, some other sexually transmitted diseases, bacteria that cause diarrhoea and other gut conditions, and the common cold. Cold viruses, rhinoviruses, get in through the mucous membrane of the nose.

A still more ingenious approach to an AIDS vaccine being tried is what is called the Anti-Idiotype vaccine. This is rather complicated but very clever – some say too clever to work. The idea is to make the vaccinated person's immune system recognize and attack just the part of the AIDS virus, HIV, that actually locks on the surface of the T-cell that the virus infects.

An HIV particle enters a T-cell at one particular spot on the cell's surface, a so-called receptor like a miniature sense organ, which is normally used by T-cells to recognize foreign viruses and other foreign enemies which have got into the body. This receptor is called CD4. An HIV particle has its own receptor which reacts specifically with the CD4 receptor, as the first step in the particle entering a T-cell. Dr Ronald Kennedy, in the Foundation for Biomedical Research in San Antonio, Texas and Dr Angus Dalgleish, in the British Clinical Research Centre at Northwick Park Hospital near London, are making vaccines which they hope will stimulate an immune reaction against the HIV receptor. If the vaccine works, antibodies formed against the receptor will lock onto it, leaving virus particles unable to enter T-cells because their receptors, which have to be free to react with T-cells' CD4 receptors, have antibodies covering them.

The problem was how to make the human immune system react specifically against the HIV receptor when no one knows which bit of the viral coat is the receptor. Dalgleish and Kennedy did it like this. First they isolated CD4 receptors from human T-cells – not too difficult a task since the CD4 receptor's structure is known – and injected a solution of receptors into mice. The mice reacted, as to any foreign substance, by making antibodies against the injected receptor material. These antibodies, because they reacted very specifically with the precise structure of the CD4 receptor, had to have the same structure as the HIV receptor, which also has to react very specifically with the CD4 receptor. There's only one structure that can do that.

The next step was to collect the antibodies to the CD4 and to use them as an experimental vaccine. Injected into animals, these antibodies caused the formation of anti-antibodies, which are also antibodies against HIV receptors. They have to be, because the thing they react with, the antibody to CD4 receptor, has the same structure as the HIV receptor. Clever.

A vaccine made in this way – from antibodies against CD4 receptor – is called not, logically, an anti-antibody vaccine but, confusingly, an anti-idiotype vaccine. The idea worked in animal experiments, but it has yet to be tested in humans. There are potential hazards in using it. The main danger comes from the fact that the vaccine stimulates the immune system to make antibodies which resemble part of the immune system's own cells, the CD4 receptor, very closely. That could lead to more antibodies being made against the CD4 receptor itself, and the immune system then mistakenly destroying T-cells that should be protecting it, in a self-destructive process similar in its effects to but much much more rapid than AIDS itself.

So great caution in following this approach will be needed, as Dr Dalgleish himself warns. But there are ways in which anti-idiotype vaccines could be further refined and made safer. One target is to identify the precise bit of the CD4 receptor to which HIV attaches and to use only this to stimulate the formation of the antibodies which are later used in a vaccine. Hopefully, this would result in the formation of antibodies which would react only with HIV, and would not cause further self-destructive reactions in the immune system.

The above are some of the ingenious approaches being followed in attempts to develop a vaccine able to protect against AIDS. Some such vaccines might also help people already infected with HIV and showing some symptoms of immune deficiency, but as yet not too many. Vaccinating such people might stimulate an immune reaction against the virus while the patient had some immune system left, and slow up or even arrest the progress of AIDS.

Vaccines, as and when they are developed may indeed play an important role in the treatment of AIDS as well as in attempts to prevent infection, since vaccines stimulate the immune system itself to combat the virus. Only the immune system so far is clever enough to single out a virus from the human body it infects. Drugs to date can't do it. You may have noted that all the attempts to make vaccines I have described depend upon genetic engineering, or the making of monoclonal antibodies, or both.

So much for vaccines for AIDS. What about drugs? Because viruses are such simple organisms, consisting only of a set of genetic instructions for making more virus enclosed in a simple, protective protein coat, they are difficult to attack with drugs. Within minutes of virus particles entering the body they have found their way into the cells they infect and, once inside a cell, the DNA from the virus behaves like that of the cell it infects, taking over control of the cell and ordering it to make more virus. So once infection is under way and virus particles have got into cells there is little that drugs can do to attack the virus without attacking the cell too.

This is true of other virus diseases besides AIDS. Once you have an ordinary cold or flu there is absolutely nothing you can do about it but eat a healthy diet and wait for the immune system to fight it off. But HIV, a retrovirus, lurks integrated into the DNA of cells where it cannot be found and attacked, and progressively destroys the immune system which should be fighting it. Wholly new approaches are needed to combat HIV. All the resources of genetic engineering and molecular medicine are being put to work to devise them.

The most effective existing drug, AZT, mimics a chemical, a base which is one of the sub-units out of which the virus assembles its genetic code. If this mimicking chemical is, so to speak, fed to the virus while it is replicating and making new DNA, the outcome is that the mimicking compound gets built into new viral DNA in place of the proper base. This then means that the virus's genetic code is defective. So when the virus tries to replicate, its genetic instructions are faulty and replication is brought to a halt.

AZT is already widely used, and while it has severe side effects which make it unusable for some patients, it can slow down and even temporarily arrest the progress of the disease condition in some people. But it is not and cannot be a cure, since it does not eradicate infection in cells which already have HIV genes inserted into their nuclei.

A different approach is to try to prevent more T-cells becoming infected, by mopping up virus particles which are produced by virus in infected cells and would otherwise infect more cells. Once again, this involves the CD4 receptor, the part of the T-cell's surface through which HIV particles enter it. The Swiss genetic engineering company Biogen has taken the gene for CD4, cloned it, and mass-produced CD4 material on its own – lots and lots of receptors without any cells. The idea is that when this CD4 is injected into AIDS patients, new HIV virus particles which are produced by the virus already infecting them will be mopped up by the injected CD4. So the progress of the disease will be stopped, or at least slowed.

Soluble CD4 used like this is now in clinical trials. Meanwhile a more sophisticated variant of the same idea has been developed, by a rival – some would say *the* rival – genetic engineering company, Genentech of California. Genentech have also made CD4 to use in the same way. But they have linked CD4 to an antibody against HIV. This was made by injecting HIV antigens into mice and doing the usual monoclonal trick to finish up with a cell culture producing the antibody as required.

Tests, so far not in humans, have shown that this hybrid has two advantages over CD4 on its own. One is that it stays in the bloodstream for much longer before being eliminated as a waste product. This would mean that, assuming the treatment proves valuable to AIDS patients, they would only have to be injected with CD4 twice a week or so rather than two or three times daily.

The other and more important advantage of the CD4-antibody hybrid, is still hypothetical at the time of writing. The hope is, that the antibody half of the combination will not only latch onto virus particles in the bloodstream more powerfully than CD4 on its own, but that it will also attack virus in cells which are already infected. When the virus is replicating, its antigens – proteins – appear on the surface of the cell it infects. Anti-HIV antibodies attached to CD4 will home onto the virus revealing itself on the surface of the infected T-cells, and mark them and the virus in them down for destruction by the immune system.

At least, this is what antibodies do in cells infected with other viruses. The only way to kill a virus integrated into a cell is to kill the cell and the virus with it. It may work for AIDS too, though it would have to be done before the disease had progressed too far, i.e. while the patient still had enough immune system left to follow up and destroy the T-cells marked down by antibodies as containing HIV.

If CD4 linked to anti-HIV antibodies *does* attack and annihilate HIV-infected cells as well as free virus particles in the blood, then it could succeed not only in slowing and arresting the progress of the disease but even in improving the patients' condition. But it will not cure AIDS. To do that must involve rooting out the virus integrated into the DNA of infected cells, which gives no sign of its presence on the cell surface or anywhere else, unless it is actively replicating. Also, HIV can spread from cell to cell by causing infected cells to fuse with non-infected cells, without leaving the cells at all and so without the virus exposing itself to attack by circulating antibodies.

Yet another problem is that HIV enters the cells of the brain and nervous system, which it sometimes infects at a late state of AIDS without going in through CD4 receptors. Whether CD4, with or without antibodies, could block infection of the nervous system is uncertain. All in all it seems most likely that if CD4 with or without antibody is beneficial, it will at best prolong the lives of AIDS patients indefinitely without preventing some decline in their condition, the sort of effect injected insulin has when used to treat diabetes.

Another technique which could perhaps stop or at least slow up the spread of HIV from cell to cell involves the use of 'Anti-Sense' RNA. One group who have been pursuing this approach is in Enzo Biochem of New York City, who have been using the technique first developed by the State University of New York. The anti-sense concept is also being used in plant biotechnology; its use there is described in the chapter on 'The Green Genes'. It depends on the fact that a single strand of DNA or RNA which is the mirror image of another such strand will be attracted right along its length to the opposite strand if they meet. They will cleave together.

When HIV genes, which have become inserted in among the genes of a T-cell infected with the virus, replicate, they do so by copying off a single strand of messenger RNA which behaves exactly like the cell's own messengers. It travels out to a ribosome

73

and is transcribed into a viral protein, as part of the process of making a new virus particle.

The anti-sense concept involves somehow inserting genes which are mirror images of HIV genes into T-cells infected with or at risk of infection with HIV. If HIV attempts to replicate within the cell then, as the HIV gene's messenger leaves the nucleus, it is liable to meet a mirror image messenger sent out from the anti-gene. The two messengers will cleave together and since transcription depends upon having a naked single strand of RNA, viral replication will be blocked. That is, assuming that the HIV gene being blocked by an anti-gene is chosen as one which produces a protein which is absolutely vital to viral replication.

The use of anti-sense genes sounds rather too pretty an idea to be realistic as an AIDS treatment. But, (as you will read in the chapter on 'Green Genes') anti-sense is already being developed fast as a commercial way of fine-tuning plant metabolism and, hopefully, as a means of improving the properties of vegetable oils. What works for such down-to-earth purposes might also help to slow the spread of infection in an AIDS patient's body and prolong his healthy life.

Of course there's the not so small problem of getting the anti-genes into the white cells. But ways of getting genes into white cells are already being developed for gene therapy, to try to cure genetic diseases which affect the immune system. Bone marrow from an AIDS patient could be taken and infected with a harmless retrovirus carrying the wanted antigenes, and reinserted into the patient.

Another technique being borrowed from plant biotechnology to try to treat AIDS is the use of ribozymes, 'Genetic Scissors' – sequences of RNA, described more fully in the chapter 'Green Genes' – which can be genetically programmed to cut up and destroy any required sets of genes. If similar techniques to those described above could be used to insert ribozymes programmed to destroy HIV genes into white cells, then the cells could be protected against HIV infection and replication.

You can see that the ability to shift genes from one organism to another, with associated technologies including, most importantly, the ability to make monoclonal antibodies to order, has produced a wide variety of ingenious contenders which may become drugs to attack and vaccines to prevent AIDS. Before genetic engineering – even ten years ago – we would have been helpless in the face of the AIDS epidemic. Now we can hope realistically for drugs to slow up and perhaps stop the progress of the disease, and there is real though longer term hope of vaccines to prevent it. Complete cures may not come in the foreseeable future.

Also vital is the new ability, using genetic engineering, to transplant a complete human immune system into mice and then to infect it with HIV. Then new drugs can be tested in the mice as if in humans. This has bridged the gap between animal and human tests.

The weapons to fight AIDS are coming from research on all kinds of other things; all the techniques which together led to gene cloning and the making of monoclonal antibodies; yeast genetics, plant virus studies . . . The history of AIDS research is one long argument against any policy which supports research only in areas seen to be of immediate benefit.

8

GENE
THERAPY

We have looked at what can be done by taking human genes out of humans and putting them into cell cultures, so as to make the body's chemical messengers; hormones and other control substances outside the body to use as medical drugs. The reverse procedure, putting 'new' genes *into* people, also holds great promise for medicine. How near are doctors to being able to use such gene therapy? What will it be used for? Are there ethical problems involved and if so what are they? These are the questions I'll try to answer in this and the next chapter.

Genes are no longer mysterious, almost mythical entities but discrete chemical sequences which are being taken apart and remade, atom by atom, in the lab. Although the mapping of the whole human genome has scarcely begun, it is already possible to identify defective genes in samples of DNA taken from a foetus, a baby or an adult who may be affected by a genetic defect. Even before the precise gene affected by a defect which causes a disease has been identified and its position on a chromosome found, it is often possible to tell whether or not a person or a foetus is affected by such a genetic defect by searching for a marker. This is a sequence of DNA which is known always to be linked to the defective gene, though it does not cause the defect.

This is making it increasingly possible to sample DNA in tests to discover whether or not a foetus is affected by a genetic defect which will cause a serious disorder if the foetus is born and grows into an adult. A woman who knows or suspects herself to be at risk of giving birth to a child with a serious genetic defect can often now take advantage of such tests to have a foetus screened at an early stage of development. A tiny sample is removed from the foetus and DNA is taken from it and compared to reference strands of DNA kept in a sort of reference library. If the foetus carries the defect, the woman can ask for it to be aborted, if it doesn't the pregnancy proceeds to term.

In this way births can be avoided of people affected by diseases which are incurable, often crippling, painful, progressive and sometimes fatal at an early age. By preventing the birth of individuals affected by genetic defects, this sort of screening can hope slowly to reduce the incidence of such defects in the population. But, since they continually recur as mutations, many genetic defects can never be eliminated by foetal tests and abortions.

There are of course violent disagreements over the use of this technique. Those, including the authorities of the Roman Catholic Church, who are opposed to all abortions, campaign against the use of foetal tests because it leads to abortion of a foetus which is affected by a defect. Those who approve the use of foetal testing do not approve it for all purposes. As knowledge of the human genome increases, so it is becoming possible to identify not only defects which will inevitably lead to serious, progressive, crippling and fatal disorders, but also genetic factors which are not potentially fatal but which make someone abnormally susceptible to conditions such as heart disease or cancer.

Doctors who approve foetal tests and abortions for conditions such as muscular dystrophy won't feel the same about liability to heart disease or cancer. But, with heart disease at least and possibly with some cancers, there are several genes involved. These provide a graduated scale of liability to disease, from a mild predisposition to virtual predestination, according to how many of the genes someone is affected by. It will become increasingly hard in these and in other similar areas for doctors to decide where they are prepared to consider testing and abortion and where they are not.

Most tests performed on foetuses today don't depend on identifying defects in individual genes, but upon spotting much grosser defects, for example part of a chromosome missing in Down's syndrome. But even now, before the mapping of the human genome has progressed very far, it is already possible to diagnose several diseases caused by genetic defects by comparing samples of genes from a foetus with 'reference library' genes.

This is because it is often possible to identify a marker, a bit of DNA which is always associated with the defect and never present when the defect is not present. There are sequences of DNA called polymorphisms, each of which is found only on one chromosome inherited from one parent. If such a polymorphism is located on the same chromosome as a defective gene which causes a disease, then the polymorphism can be used to trace the defect through successive generations. It reveals who has the defect and who does not before the defective gene itself is localized on the chromosome.

It is now possible to identify several genetic defects before birth using either polymorphisms or, in two or three cases now, the actual genetic defect involved. These techniques are generally accepted for use – outside the religious groups who object to abortion on principle. They will make a growing impact on medicine in the near future.

As infectious diseases have continued to be eliminated, in Western countries at least, so conditions caused by genetic defects have become more important as causes of ill-health and death. While infant mortality in the UK has declined from 154 deaths per 1000 in 1900 to 16 per 1000 in 1984, the percentage of such deaths attributable to genetic abnormalities has risen from 5 per cent to 30 per cent. About 5.5 per cent of the British population are now affected at some time in their lives by ill-health attributed to genetic factors. That figure is rising rapidly as susceptibility to more diseases, including heart disease and cancers is found to be genetically determined.

More that 2000 human diseases are known to be caused by defects in single genes. This makes it potentially possible to diagnose all of them by a simple DNA test, and then to eliminate affected foetuses. The fact that the genes affected by such defects are now beginning to be localized on chromosomes also suggests the possibility of gene therapy, of inserting correct genes to compensate for defective ones. Defects in single genes are potentially more susceptible to gene therapy than defects in multiple genes, because it is much easier to insert a single gene into cells that lack the gene than it is to insert several genes, each perhaps having to be placed in the right position relative to all the others. That is what may be needed for gene therapy for disorders where more than one gene is affected.

But more about gene therapy later. First we are concerned with the diagnosis of genetic defects, and their elimination by abortion. One of the first significant advances in genetic diagnosis came in 1983, Dr James Guesella of the Massachusetts General Hospital developed a test, using a polymorphism, which can identify with more than 99 per cent accuracy those individuals in a family at risk who are going to develop Huntingtons Chorea. This condition causes rapidly progressive mental disease in middle age, for which there is at present no treatment. The development of the test able to identify those who will develop a fatal disease for which there is no cure and no treatment, has caused fierce controversy. Many people at risk prefer not to have the test and others complain about its availability for use by insurance companies.

Other polymorphisms have been identified for use in prenatal tests for the most common form of haemophilia, haemophilia A; for the most disabling form of the muscle-weakening disease muscular dystrophy, Duchenne muscular dystrophy, DMD; and for the commonest form of thalassaemia, a form of anaemia caused by genetic defects. Meanwhile the actual genetic defects which are responsible for disease conditions are being tracked down. On Christmas Eve 1987 Doctors Eric Hoffman and Lewis Kunkel of the Harvard Medical School announced that they had pinpointed the gene which is defective or absent in Duchenne muscular dystrophy, DMD. This enabled them also to identify the protein – part of the muscle tissue – which the gene is the blueprint for and which is therefore also defective or absent in DMD.

This was a great moment in the history of medical molecular biology. It was the first time that the beautifully remorseless detective work which is used to track down individual genes had succeeded first in identifying a gene which is defective in a disease, and then in locating and identifying the protein made by the gene which is defective or absent in the disease and the absence of which causes the disease. The achievement showed that it has become possible to bypass the laborious business of analysing endless proteins in tissues in search of abnormalities in genetically-caused diseases, and instead to go straight for the defect and to identify it at the molecular level.

It was done for DMD, and is being done for other genetic diseases by seeking out and locating the defective gene, sequencing that gene, working out from the gene sequence the precise corresponding chemical structure of the protein the gene is the blueprint for, and then seeking that protein in the human body. The whole process takes a year or two. But it must lead infallibly to the individual protein molecule, out of the many thousands of different protein molecules in the human body, which is defective in a particular disease caused by a particular genetic defect.

Once the protein is pinpointed its normal function can be seen, or deduced. Then rational ways to treat the condition can be devised. It may be done by compensating for the missing or damaged protein's absent function, or by inserting the missing protein in the cells where it is missing, or by inserting the correct version of the defective gene into the cells where its absence is causing problems. All the possibilities can be devised and tested until one of them works.

How many of the 2000 human diseases caused by defects in single genes it will be possible to do this for, is still unknown. But the identifying of Dystrophin – as the protein which is defective in DMD has been christened – has shown that the whole idea, which would have been wild fantasy twenty years ago, actually works. The gene which is defective in DMD was identified. The gene was cloned and its product dystrophin, the protein the gene is the blueprint for, was made by the cloned gene. The dystrophin was injected into animals which made antibodies against it, which reacted only with dystrophin.

These antibodies, made as monoclonal antibodies, were then used to search for dystrophin in samples of human muscle taken from DMD patients and from normal people. Dystrophin was present in the normal people but absent in the DMD patients. The antibodies revealed where dystrophin is located in muscles. From its position the scientists are now working out dystrophin's function in muscle, and what happens when it is missing or defective, i.e. what really goes wrong in the bodies of DMD patients.

Exactly what dystrophin does is still unknown. But there are clues. Dystrophin and its gene are, as biologists say, highly conserved. That is, dystrophin and the gene for it are found in exactly the same form in every animal that had been studied so far, including frogs, chickens and mice – as well as humans. So clearly the protein does something very vital and very universal in muscle.

More evidence for this is provided by the huge size – on a molecular scale – of this gene and protein. Compared to an average protein – the insulin molecule for example – the molecule of dystrophin is the size of a football compared to a marble. The bigger a gene, the more there is to go wrong with it and the more likely it is to suffer a mutation – a random change. The fact that this enormous gene is found in exactly the same form in so many different animals in spite of it being so accident-prone, means it must fulfil some very important function, which depends vitally on the structure of the dystrophin molecule. If its structure was less essential then dystrophin would not be so highly conserved, and something less accident-prone would have evolved in its place.

The vulnerability of the gene is the reason why doctors cannot hope to eliminate muscular dystrophy by testing foetuses for defective genes and aborting those affected. New mutations continually arise unpredictably in unaffected people, who then give birth quite unexpectedly to babies affected by the condition.

One approach to therapy for DMD which is now possible and is in progress is to work out the function of dystrophin and try to find some way of compensating for its absence. Another approach is to see if nature has already found a way to compensate for defective dystrophin. A group at the Hammersmith Hospital in West London are studying mice which inherit a defect identical to that which causes DMD in humans. These mice have no dystrophin in their muscles at all. When they are two or three weeks old, they begin to show symptoms like those of human DMD. Their muscles begin to weaken. But then the condition stops progressing and regresses. The mouse recovers and develops more or less normally for the rest of its life.

Some biochemical trick evolved by mice must make this possible. Now the search is on to identify the trick and see if it can somehow be transplanted into DMD patients.

Even before it leads to any treatment for DMD, the discovery of dystrophin is already providing other benefits. Genetic tests for a defective or missing dystrophin gene can now replace tests using polymorphisms and can determine earlier and with 100 per cent rather than 99 per cent reliability whether or not a foetus is affected by DMD. Tests for dystrophin itself can also be used to make a very early diagnosis of DMD in a child. As we noted earlier, because of the size of the gene and its vulnerability to mutation, the DMD defect keeps cropping up afresh, so that, sadly, there will always be children born suffering from it to unsuspecting mothers. At the Hammersmith Hospital in London, when a mother brings in a child with early signs of muscle weakening, doctors can now take a muscle sample the size of a matchhead and test it to see if any dystrophin is present. If it is then the infant is not suffering from DMD. If there is no dystrophin or defective dystrophin, then the child is affected.

Having such a definite diagnosis early either dispels unnecessary fears or helps mothers and families to come to terms with the situation. By giving warning of the possibility of another birth affected by DMD, it can also prevent it happening by revealing the need for foetal testing.

Most exciting of all, further new treatments are now envisaged. Early diagnosis will be important because the new treatments are likely to be more effective the earlier they are attempted. For several years Dr Terence Partridge of the Charing Cross and Westminster Hospitals' Medical Schools in London has been working towards the long-term target of treating muscular dystrophy by grafting healthy muscle tissue into muscles affected by the disease. He and others have found that when healthy muscle cells are so implanted, they fuse with the cells affected by the condition, forming giant hybrid cells with numerous nuclei, known as syncytia, which behave as healthy cells.

A potential problem in using this approach in treatment is knowing how effective the treatment is being. When Dr Partridge read of Kunkel's breakthrough in identifying dystrophin, he suggested a collaboration with the aim of using Partridge's muscle-grafting techniques to try to put cells that make dystrophin into muscle that lacks it, using dystrophin itself as a marker to see how far the treatment was working.

Work along these lines has been going on and only about a year after Kunkel and Hoffman's first report of the discovery of dystrophin, Partridge and Kunkel reported some exciting first results from animal experiments. The scientists used healthy foetal muscle precursor cells, cells which would later have formed muscle, taken from foetal mice. These were injected into the dystrophin-deficient muscles of mice affected by an inherited condition which closely mimics DMD. The implanted cells fused with muscle cells forming syncytia which produced dystrophin.

Problems will have to be overcome before the same technique could be tried on human DMD patients. Huge numbers of healthy human muscle cells would have to be grown in culture ready for use. These would have to be taken from aborted human foetuses. Adult muscle cells would fuse less easily with the patient's own muscle cells, and would be more likely to be rejected as foreign tissue. Whether aborted foetuses will in the future be made available as sources of material for therapy is uncertain. Doctors and scientists are hoping for legislation and guidelines permitting the use of foetal tissue under controlled conditions. But new legislation may forbid its use in the UK.

Another problem is that a very large number of injections of foetal cells, perhaps spaced as closely as one centimetre apart, might be needed to get dystrophin-making cells into enough of a baby's muscles to be worthwhile. But once injected, as early as possible in life, presumably under mild anaesthetic, the nuclei of the injected cells containing the vital genes for producing dystrophin would hopefully continue to divide along with the baby's own cell nuclei in syncytia inside growing and developing muscle tissue.

As with all foreign tissue implants, rejection could be a problem. But the first tests on mice suggest that it may be less of a problem than with other organ and tissue transplants and that rejection may be lessened by the use of foetal material. If foetal cells cannot be used then it might be possible to use ordinary connective tissue cells, grown in culture with added dystrophin genes as an alternative for implants.

A big problem with no apparent solution at present is how to get the injected cells into the heart muscle, which is affected by DMD like other muscle. But these are early days. What can be said now is, that there is real hope of a treatment for DMD sufferers which will at least improve their condition, though it is too early to say when it may become available. One point made by the researchers is that there is no point in trying this treatment in a primitive form for such cases – even in desperate cases – because sadly it undoubtedly wouldn't work. More research is needed before doctors can be sure enough of possible benefits to try it in less advanced cases of DMD, in view of both possible side effects and of the possibility that other treatments may become available.

This approach to therapy for a disease caused by a genetic defect is unusual. It is based on the unique ability of muscle cells to fuse and form syncytia. In other parts of the body affected by other genetic defects, injected cells generally would not fuse with the affected person's own cells. Cells which did not fuse would be liable to be strongly rejected as foreign material. But one way to avoid the problem of rejection in treating some such conditions may be to inject healthy cells long before birth.

Tests for defective genes can be carried out using samples taken from what are called the chorionic villi, part of the innermost membrane surrounding the foetus. Samples of chorionic villi can be taken as early as eight weeks into pregnancy. This makes therapeutic abortion safer and less traumatic for the woman involved than abortion performed after the test mainly used today, amniocentesis, which is carried out at a much later stage. It also opens up the prospect of therapy before birth as an alternative to abortion for some genetic diseases.

The human foetus only begins to acquire its own immune system – making it able to recognize and reject foreign tissue – at about eighteen weeks after conception. So if a genetic defect affecting the bone marrow, or affecting the red or white blood cells which are made by bone marrow, is diagnosed at eight or nine weeks into pregnancy from a chorionic villus sample, then it is potentially possible, using techniques already used for other purposes, to give the foetus a blood transfusion which will cure the defect.

A foetus with a genetic defect affecting bone marrow could be given a blood transfusion containing healthy bone marrow cells from a healthy donor. These cells would naturally find their way to and populate the foetal bone marrow. Foreign tissue implanted before the immune system is developed is always regarded as 'self' and never rejected. Bone marrow cells have a natural homing instinct, they automatically travel to and settle down inside the body's big bones.

A foetus given such injections long before birth would grow up as what scientists call a 'chimaera'. That is, a person containing cells derived from two different sources, the foetus itself and the bone marrow donor. If all went well the healthy donor bone marrow cells would supply enough healthy red or white cells throughout life to compensate for the defect affecting the foetus's own red or white blood cells.

This technique would require no genetic engineering, but the other arm of the medical biotechnology revolution – the making of monoclonal antibodies – would be needed to make it work. This is because, although the foetus, not having developed an immune system, would be unable to recognize and reject the foreign bone marrow cells injected into it, the injected cells would be able to recognize and reject their new host, the foetus. Bone marrow cells constantly divide to manufacture the cells of the immune system, the white blood cells which patrol the body looking for foreign tissue to attack. From the point of view of white cells produced by the implanted bone marrow, the entire living environment they found themselves inside would be foreign. There would be what transplant surgeons call a 'graft-versus-host' or GVH reaction, which would continually ravage the body of the growing foetus, and, later, the person it grew into.

In order to prevent the GVH reaction, what is needed is some way to remove just the cells which are liable to provoke GVH from the donor bone marrow before implanting it, leaving the rest intact. Monoclonal antibodies make this possible. Members of the class of white cells which cause the GVH reaction can be isolated and injected into mice, which react by making antibodies against the cells. The mouse cells making the antibodies can be made into an 'immortal' culture in the usual way, producing the antibodies for as long as they are required as monoclonal antibodies. These antibodies can then be used to pick out and destroy all the cells liable to cause GVH in a sample of bone marrow, before it is injected into a foetus to cure a genetic defect affecting bone marrow.

There is nothing futuristic about any of these techniques. They are all already in use for other purposes; chorionic villus sampling is used to diagnose genetic defects and foetal blood transfusions are used to treat 'rhesus babies', in which problems are caused by differences between foetal and maternal blood groups. Monoclonal antibodies are already being used to remove cells liable to cause GVH reactions from bone marrow before implanting it into children or adults to treat leukaemia. All that is necessary is to combine the techniques. A group led by Dr Charles Rodeck in Kings College Hospital in London hopes to do so in the not-too-distant future.

Making a foetus into a chimaera to treat a genetic defect rather than aborting it, could avoid the need for abortions and so satisfy the demands of some religious groups, as well as avoiding the trauma of an abortion for the woman involved. But it will only work for a few conditions. If such prenatal treatments ever came into use on a large scale, then they would store up growing problems for the future. At present the incidence of genetic defects causing serious illness tends to be reduced in the population, either by early death, failure to reproduce or by foetal diagnosis and abortion. If such defects became curable on a large scale, then more and more people would grow up apparently healthy but still carrying defective genes in all their own cells, masked by the population of healthy cells whose ancestors had been grafted into the people involved while they still were in the womb.

Chimaeric people could marry and have children normally. But their children would be at risk of the same genetic defect. Prenatal treatment for genetic defects could, if it became common, put an end to the gradual reduction in the incidence of some genetic defects and cause the numbers of those affected to increase again.

Religious groups which refuse abortion but allow prenatal treatment must then face the fact that their policies will lead to the spread rather than the elimination of genetic defects among those who follow their teachings, especially since new defects often arise spontaneously to join those which are inherited. The effect of a system which does away with both natural selection and abortion as means of eliminating defects, while permitting ingenious techniques for masking defects during an individual's lifetime, must ultimately be to increase the incidence of the defects. More of that in the chapter about the 'Ethics of Gene Therapy'.

So far we have talked only about injected cells (cell therapy), not injected genes (gene therapy). There is still another area where cell therapy may cure disease, though it may need genetic engineering to make it effective. This is in the treatment of brain conditions and mental illnesses.

Attempts to treat Parkinson's disease have already begun. Foetal brain cells are being used in the hope that they will produce the brain chemical, dopamine, which is deficient in Parkinsonism. The white cells of the immune system do not penetrate into the brain, they are kept out by the so-called blood-brain barrier. This means that rejection of foreign cells in the brain is much less powerful than in other parts of the body – indeed it may not occur at all. No conclusive results from this experimental treatment have yet been reported. If it is even moderately successful as a new means of therapy, its use is likely to expand and cell therapy of this kind will soon be tried for other conditions, including Alzheimers disease.

This would lead to an enormous demand for foetal brain tissue which the supply of aborted foetuses will be unable to meet, leading to the likelihood of such abuses as women being paid to become pregnant and abort foetuses to use as sources of transplant material. Genetic engineering may be able to supply an alternative.

Experiments are already going on in which ordinary human skin cells (fibroblasts), grown in laboratory culture have had extra genes for brain chemicals inserted into them and have produced the brain chemicals. Fibroblasts treated in this way so as to produce brain chemicals which are deficient might be used to treat a number of brain conditions more effectively than foetal brain cells. The fibroblasts could be given enough extra genes to make them produce relatively large amounts of the missing chemicals. Genetic engineering might also be used to remove antigens by deleting genes from the fibroblasts. This would prevent them from being recognized as foreign by the immune system.

It may prove possible to use cell therapy to cure defects in other parts of the body, including conditions caused by genetic defects. But cell therapy will remain the exception rather than the rule. For most genetic defects the hope for the future must lie in gene therapy rather than cell therapy. All genes in all higher organisms, let alone in human beings are made of the same substance – DNA. They all speak the same language. And genes can be transplanted from any organism into any other organism *without rejection*. However difficult gene therapy may prove to be in practice, these simple facts make it an enormously exciting and worthwhile target to aim for.

The way ahead for gene therapy is fairly clear. What is needed is a guidance system which will take millions of cloned copies of the correct version of a defective gene, and deliver them into the right position in the correct chromosome in the nuclei of a high proportion of the cells in the part of the body where the defect has its effect. A genetic defect is usually found in every cell of an affected person's body, because all the billions of cells in that body are derived by cell division from one single fertilized egg cell which carried the defect. However, as only a small proportion of the genes in a cell are active, a defect in a gene only matters where that gene would normally be expressed (i.e. where the gene's product is necessary for the body's proper functioning). If the correct version of a defective gene can somehow be inserted into the cells in the part of the body where that gene is expressed, then there is no need to insert the correct gene anywhere else.

If and when this becomes possible, it will cure only the person involved. Like the injection of cells described earlier, gene therapy affecting a small part of the body won't stop the person involved handing on genetic defects to their descendants. The only thing that would do that would be a technique for somehow injecting the correct version of the defective gene into all the cells in the person's ovaries or testes, the cells which go on to make sperms or eggs. That concept is known as germ line gene therapy, because the cells that form sperms and eggs are known as germ line cells. Gene therapy which only aims to correct a defect in one part of a person's body and so for only one generation is known as somatic gene therapy.

The first attempt to cure a genetic disease by somatic gene therapy will probably be an attempt to cure the disease called Lesch-Nyhans syndrome, after the doctors who first characterized it. Lesch-Nyhans syndrome, which affects only boys, causes horrible symptoms, at first tremors, weakness and jerky uncontrollable movements, then kidney damage, then bizarre self mutilation in which affected children bite off their own lips and the entire tips of their fingers.

Doctors Inder Verma and Dusty Miller of the Salk Institute and Douglas Jolly and Theodore Friedmann of the University of California at San Diego have gone a long way towards making gene therapy for Lesch-Nyhans syndrome a reality. The first need is for what genetic engineers call a vector, something which will carry the wanted gene right into the chromosomes of cells affected by the genetic defect which causes the disease. Like most other scientists working on gene therapy, Verma and Miller plan to use retroviruses as their vectors. These are viruses that insert their own genes right into the chromosomes of the cells they infect. The genes of the virus become effectively part of the cell's own genes.

Boys suffering from Lesch-Nyhans syndrome lack the gene for an essential enzyme, with a very long name but known as HPRT. Doctors Verma and Miller inserted the gene for HPRT into a retrovirus that naturally infects human cells, took samples of living cells from a person suffering from Lesch-Nyhans syndrome, and used the virus to infect the cells, grown in culture in the lab. It worked. The retrovirus injected the HPRT gene along with its own genes into the cells whose own HPRT gene was missing, and the cells began to make HPRT. They made as much of it as normal, healthy cells.

That was done in 1983. At that time it looked as if successful human gene therapy was just around the corner. But there has proved to be a big gap between repairing defects in cells in laboratory cultures and repairing them in the bodies of patients. The effects of the retroviruses being developed as vectors are to some extent unpredictable. They could cause cancers. Some other retroviruses do cause serious diseases, among them AIDS and forms of cancer. The genetic engineers hope they have made the vector viruses harmless by removing the genes which allow the virus to replicate in cells – leaving only the genes which burrow into the chromosomes carrying the inserted HPRT gene with them. But the viruses remain largely unknown quantities. The scientists are still worried that even the non-replicating retrovirus may contain, hidden among its thousands of genes, other semi-independent viruses, so-called 'helper' viruses, which could restore the retrovirus's ability to replicate and, perhaps, to cause disease.

Another problem is how to get genes for HPRT not just into cells in laboratory cultures but into the cells in the brain of Lesch-Nyhans patients, where the deficiency of the enzyme has its effect. At present an agent able to target genes to brain cells is completely lacking, though that is not to say that one can't be devised. It may be possible to get over this by inserting the genes into other cells which move to the brain early in development. But that is only a possibility.

More immediately hopeful are the prospects for using gene therapy to correct defects in the red or white blood cells of the body, defects which cause haemophilias or immune deficiencies. This is because these cells are made by cell division from cells called stem cells in the bone marrow, and it is potentially easy to get cells with added genes into the bone marrow. It will involve taking cells from the patient's bone marrow with a syringe, using a retrovirus carrying the correct version of the defective gene to infect the cells in a laboratory dish, growing the cells and injecting them back into the patient's bloodstream, when they will migrate naturally to the bone marrow.

It is also possible to give cells treated in this way other, extra

GENE SHIFTERS

Dr Michael Wilson, plant virus toolbox investigator.

Dr David Bishop uses caterpillar viruses to make drugs.

Professor David Hopwood designs new antibiotics.

Professor Alan Fersht engineers enzymes.

Dr Susan Kingsman and Dr Alan Kingsman, co-directors of the Virus Molecular Biology Group in the Department of Biochemistry.

Dr Greg Winter reshapes antibodies to attack cancer.

Right: Professor Ken Murray works on new hepatitis vaccines.

Below: Dr John Clark with a flock of transgenic sheep. (The Scotsman)

Dr Charlie Shaw protects plants against pests.

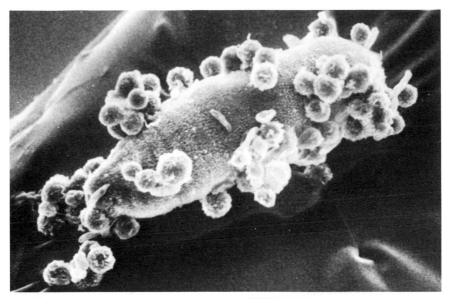

Schistosome parasite being attacked by immune cells. (Dr Diana McLaren)

Scanning electron micrograph of a human T-cell infected with the Human Immune Virus which causes AIDS. Spherical virus particles on the surface are budding away to infect more cells. (Science Photo Library)

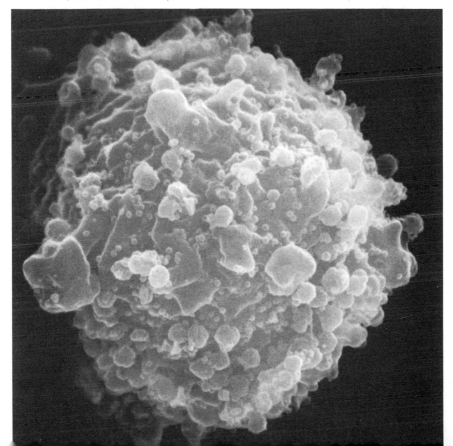

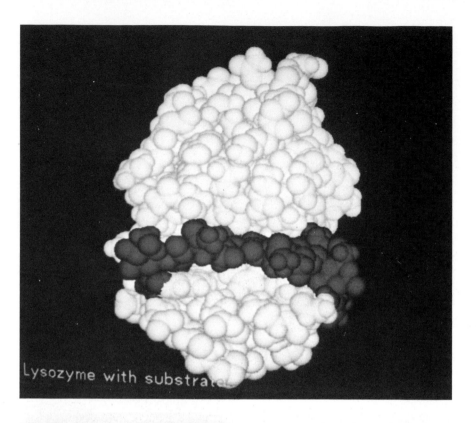

Lysozyme with substrate

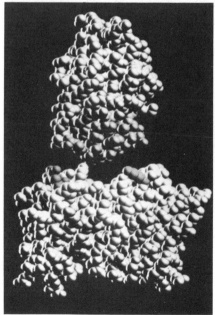

Molecular computer graphic image of an enzyme, lysozyme, interacting with its substrate, a polysaccharide, which forms part of bacterial cell walls. (Science Photo Library)

Molecular computer graphic of an antibody-antigen complex. At top is the antigen; at bottom the antibody produced in response to the antigen. The antigen molecule is hen egg white lysozyme. (Science Photo Library)

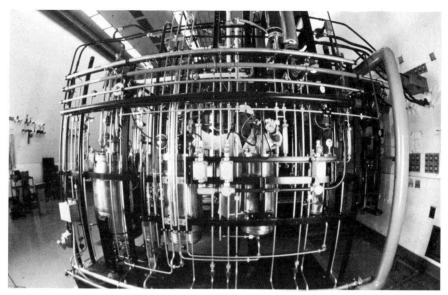

A commercial bioreactor. (Science Photo Library)

A gene sequencing machine. ARMS – the Automatic Reagent Manipulating System – developed at the Manchester Biotechnology Centre by Dr Liam Martin, left. He is demonstrating it to instrument engineer, Mr Wen-Bin He.

Specialized High-containment Laboratory at PHLS Centre for Applied Microbiology and Research. (PHLS)

This sheep/goat chimaera represents an example of inter-species chimaerism. It was produced by mixing cells of sheep and goat embryos. [Fehilly, CB, Willadsen, SM & Tucker, EM (1984) Nature, Lond. 307, 634]. AFRC Institute of Animal Physiology & Genetics Research, Cambridge.

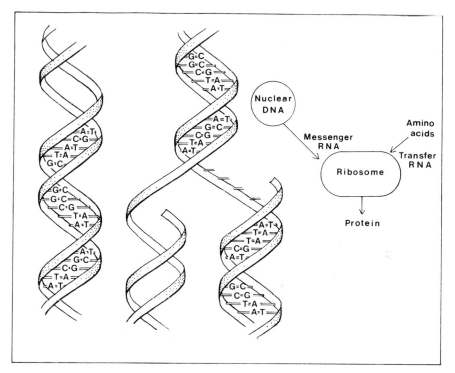

Left: *part of a DNA double helix with paired complementary bases holding the spirals together.*

Centre: *the double helix untwists to replicate and new complementary strands form around each untwisted strand.*

Right: *DNA is transcribed into RNA and translated into protein made from amino acids brought to the ribosome by transfer RNA.* (Carole Vincer)

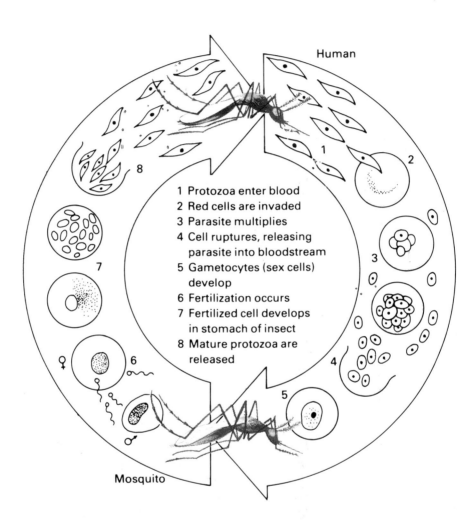

Human

1 Protozoa enter blood
2 Red cells are invaded
3 Parasite multiplies
4 Cell ruptures, releasing
  parasite into bloodstream
5 Gametocytes (sex cells)
  develop
6 Fertilization occurs
7 Fertilized cell develops
  in stomach of insect
8 Mature protozoa are
  released

Mosquito

genes which make them highly competitive inside the bone marrow, so that they will compete with and replace cells carrying the genetic defect which have not been infected with the correct gene. In this way the entire bone marrow could be populated with healthy stem cells replacing those with a genetic defect.

This technique looked set for the first human tests three years ago, but then problems appeared. The first trials were planned to treat a fatal and incurable disease caused by a defect in the gene for a vital enzyme – ADA – produced by white blood cells. But the retrovirus vector into which the gene for ADA had been spliced delivered the gene into random positions in the DNA of the stem cells in the bone marrow, and the gene didn't work. Until the gene can be inserted into the right position (or perhaps into one of a number of possible right positions,) it won't work properly to make its product, the missing enzyme ADA.

Clearly, two things are needed. Vectors that will take genes into the right parts of the body and see that they are switched on there and only there. And some means of directing genes to just the right sites in chromosomes. In fact there are now strong hopes of achieving both these aims.

One way of getting genes to work in the right part of the body is to remove cells from that part of the body, use a vector to add in the genes, and then reinsert the cells back where they came from. This is how blood cell diseases caused by genetic defects will be treated. But there are other more sophisticated techniques. Genes are naturally made to work in the part of the body where they are needed, and not in other parts of the body, by control sequences of DNA which switch the genes on where they are needed and keep them switched off elsewhere. These control sequences could be added to inserted genes to make them work in the right place and nowhere else, even though the genes were inserted into most or all of the cells of the body. Such sequences are already being used artificially to cause human body control substances to be produced into the milk of sheep, but not elsewhere in the sheep's body (See the chapter on the 'Pharmaceutical Farmyard').

The other problem – that of getting genes to the right sites on chromosomes – looks more difficult at first sight. But it may not be since it is clear that this is not always a problem. Plenty of genes work adequately when they are inserted into nuclei completely at random, (even by firing them in on a tungsten sphere, see 'The Green Genes'!) and ways to target genes to the right place in a chromosome when that is necessary are being developed. Using a technique more fully described in the chapter on transgenic animals ('The Pharmaceutical Farmyard') Dr David Melton and others have shown that by attaching a targetting sequence of DNA to a gene to be implanted, it is possible to direct that gene to a site in a chromosome next to a sequence identical to the targetting sequence.

At present gene therapy is concentrating on defects in single genes. But in the future it will move to try to cure conditions caused by defects in several genes, such as forms of thalassaemia. Experiments in mice suggest that a combination of the adaptibility of the human genome to cope with unexpected insertions, plus Melton's and other techniques for gene targetting, may soon achieve a sufficient degree of accuracy in positioning added genes to allow them to do their job and treat such conditions adequately for one generation. But such hit-and-miss techniques would certainly not be adequate for genes inserted with the aim of handing them on to future generations. Will that ever be possible or ethical? That's one of the questions for the next chapter.

9

THE ETHICS
OF GENE THERAPY

The idea of human genetic engineering – *any* human genetic engineering for any purpose – is deeply repugnant to some people. It is disquieting to many others. People do not have to understand the structure of DNA to feel that genetic engineering is a way of altering nature and ourselves which is different in kind from any other biological or medical technique. People with no formal religion, atheists even, may have an uneasy sense that to take genes from one living creature and put them into another, especially into a human, is to take an irrevocable step to assuming new responsibilities which traditionally have belonged to God, or at least to powers or forces other than ourselves. Many people may consciously or half-unconsciously expect retribution like the fate that overtook Prometheus.

As usual with deep popular misgivings, the public is right to think that something new and tremendous and disturbing is happening and that powers are being unlocked that are so potent as to deserve respect bordering on fear. I hope this book makes that clear. But the truth is that, properly used, genetic engineering will very soon do a vast amount of good; in medicine, agriculture and industry, in curing and preventing disease, in growing more and better food and in producing chemicals more cheaply and more safely. Its immediate potential for good is far, far greater than its potential for harm. But the fear is there, and because it is based on the certainty that something new and different has happened, it will not go away until the public has assimilated and mastered genetic engineering, got on top of it, become DNA-literate.

For the time being, for the next twenty, thirty, forty years genetic engineers are in the happy position of being able to do a lot of good and not much harm. Only fear based on ignorance will stop the good happening. Ignorance too will be responsible for mis-uses of genetic engineering. Full-scale public awareness would soon lead to national or international legislation to prevent commercial greed being allowed seriously to delay the benefits of breakthroughs in human or plant genetic engineering reaching those in need, in the forms of new vaccines, drought resistant crops and so on.

For the time being the real problem is not ethical but educa-tional. Scientists have broken through to an extraordinary truth, that a simple self-replicating chemical called DNA made of just four different chemical groupings, or *bases* has invented every form of life on Earth; the elephant, the whale, the fungus, the oak tree and you and me and that by rearranging those four bases we can rearrange life to suit ourselves as easily as the bases them-selves have rearranged it to suit their own blind un-conscious drive to replicate. For example, viral genes use promoters to make more viral genes, we use promoters to make vaccines to fight viruses.

This truth is so enormous that almost the only people who have grasped it are the genetic engineers themselves and the few who work directly with them. As they forge ahead with ever-growing confidence into the second generation of advanced engineering, the public at large is still slowly assimilating the scale of the breakthrough. Until assimilation is complete and education has begun to catch up, a pall of ignorance causing fear and repug-nance will continue to hang over genetic engineering. In Britain the consequence may be that industry will hesitate to invest, fearing public opinion. Impressionable students will choose other careers, politicians will be wary of backing measures that could lose them votes. Ignorant proposals fervently put forward by ignorant men blocking research will slide into legislation. We in Britain will lose out on something for which we have all the resources to succeed overwhelmingly, and we will finish up having to buy it back from other nations. That is, unless we can educate the public in time.

Education, not ethics is the problem today. But as the ability to alter the human genome in controlled ways progresses – and it is going to progress very fast now – in perhaps less than fifty years the real ethical problems will begin to surface. Indeed this is the other argument for education – for DNA-literacy – so as to be prepared for the time when the hard choices have to be made in the grey areas. They ought to be made by a responsible electorate, not by a few secretive establishment figures in a committee room.

In undemocratic systems of government, other and worse things need to be anticipated so as to prevent them if possible. What would Hitler have done with genetic engineering had it arrived fifty years earlier – used Jews for genetic experiments? Attempted to improve genetically on the master race? The grip of Lysenko's genetics in the Soviet Union, which harked back to the pre-Darwinian belief that characteristics acquired by a plant during its life could be inherited by its offspring, as well as Hitler's racial theories on Nazi Germany, show how science can be deliberately misinterpreted to serve evil or lunatic causes. In other areas of science history is full of examples of rulers who listened not to the best scientific advisers but to those who told them what they wanted to believe to suit their wishes.

The truth is that eventually – which probably means in about fifty years time – genetic engineering is going to put enormous power to change ourselves into the hands of humans. It is up to us, as always of course, to prevent the establishment of dictatorships, where such powers can be misused without democratic safeguards. But within democracies, it is essential to have an informed electorate, so that decisions are made by the peoples' representatives in accordance with the people's wishes.

An editorial in the *Lancet*, the leading medical weekly (28 January 1989) put it well. 'What one needs is an educated public. They need to be sufficiently DNA-literate to appraise the advantages and disadvantages of gene therapy. The more people involved in the decision-making processes the better. Decisions should not be confined to a small group of experts, be they scientists or politicians, philosophers or doctors.'

With that preamble, what are the issues involved in human genetic engineering in gene therapy? Two kinds of gene therapy are possible. First, somatic therapy, in which genes are added to someone to try to cure just him or her of a condition caused by a genetic defect. Somatic gene therapy involves finding some way to direct the correct version of a defective gene to just the part of the body where its absence is causing disease. It does not involve inserting genes into germ cells – reproductive cells – so that the genes are handed onto the next generation.

That is the province of the second kind of gene therapy – germ line gene therapy. This, if it is carried out will attempt not just to cure individuals of genetic defects but also to lift the shadows of such defects from the lives of all those individuals' descendants. Somatic therapy is generally favoured by doctors, germ line therapy is generally condemned as unethical interference. But both are now possible for some conditions, though still untried and with a low potential success rate at the present stage of development.

Preparations are now being made for the first serious attempts at human somatic gene therapy. They were described in the last chapter. The usual ethical constraints which govern any radically new treatment will be observed. Because of possible unpredictable side effects (perhaps of the added gene itself, perhaps of the virus used as a vector to get it into human cells) the treatments will be introduced cautiously, starting with patients who are in desperate need and for whom there is no alternative.

For some genetic diseases these problems will be less onerous than they are for some other new treatments, for cancers for example. Because genes are natural agents that work in the same way in mice as they do in men, their effects are likely to be highly predictable. And since there are no cures for genetic diseases, it will not be hard to find groups of patients who may benefit from gene therapy and will certainly die without it.

It is not surprising that somatic gene therapy is overwhelmingly approved by doctors and others who understand it. It is indeed hard to see how anyone could object to curing tragically crippling, progressive and fatal diseases, which are standing out more and more as infectious diseases come under control. The only informed objections that will be raised will be by those who argue that unless all gene therapy is forbidden, not only will somatic therapy lead on down a 'slippery slope' to germ line therapy, (of which more later,) but also that somatic gene therapy will be used for increasingly frivolous or even immoral purposes, as the ability to use it in such ways is acquired.

The first argument can be discounted. It is easy to make a firm distinction between somatic–body cells and germ line–reproductive cells. Most doctors and scientists involved are already making the distinction and approving gene therapy for one while disapproving of it for the other. The second argument really means no more than that somatic gene therapy will require the same regulation as any other new technique. It may for example turn out to be the case that, as well as curing genetic diseases, actual genes implanted into people are able to make them more sexually attractive or more sexually active. (At present it seems more likely that gene products cloned outside the body will do such things, but that may change.)

As with plastic surgery, it will be necessary to prevent the public from being misled by exaggerated claims and to ensure that limited national as opposed to private resources are not spent on such things. But these are not new problems. If people want gene therapy for what others consider to be frivolous purposes, they are as entitled to pay for it as they are to pay for other therapy of little real benefit. Similarly, gene therapy used for illegal or immoral purposes, to give athletes unfair advantages in contests for example, would need to be regulated as ordinary drugs are today. There are no new problems involved, just new examples of old ones.

As time goes on, one effect that somatic gene therapy will have is to widen the gulf between those whose religious beliefs condemn abortion and those who permit it. For strict Catholics, today's growing ability to diagnose genetic defects before birth, coupled with tomorrow's growing ability to cure such defects in the affected individual, will lead to more and more children being born affected by defects. Women will be less tempted to resort to forbidden abortion if a baby can be cured by gene therapy.

Some cures will be possible before birth. Last June a French surgeon, Professor Jean-Louis Touraine transplanted foetal cells to an unborn baby to cure a disease of the immune system caused by a genetic defect. The mother had already had one baby born with the defect and preferred the pre-natal transplant to an abortion. Many more women will prefer gene therapy or cell therapy (the two will anyhow become hard to distinguish as extra genes are inserted into cells used for cell therapy!) to be given to the baby before or after birth, to the trauma of prenatal testing followed by repeated abortions. Indeed many women with no religious convictions against abortion will prefer the less traumatic course of therapy.

The medical profession generally however will surely argue the other way. They will argue for foetal testing for defects followed by early abortion if women request it. Techniques now being developed allow genetic tests to be performed on eggs fertilized and grown to the very early embryo stage outside the body, so that only those embryos with no defects are then reimplanted to develop. For women with anticipated defects this avoids any need for abortion in the usual sense. It will be a more acceptable process for the women involved – but the disposal of the defective embryos still represents abortion from the strict Catholic standpoint.

For those who accept abortion, the combination of prenatal tests with DNA probes giving earlier and more reliable results, plus early abortion or *in vitro* (outside the body) fertilization doing away with abortion altogether, will lead to a steady decrease in the incidence of genetic defects. But there will always be a need for somatic gene therapy, because some defects continually crop up as random mutations, as in muscular dystrophy for example.

For those who do not accept abortion, on the other hand, new techniques must lead to the birth of more and more people affected by genetic defects. Coexistence will become more difficult, as the pro-abortionists protest against paying the high cost of somatic gene therapy for the growing numbers of people in need. As medical progress continues and infectious diseases are increasingly eliminated, genetic diseases will increasingly stand out and the gulf between pro– and anti-abortionists will grow.

The tests that already exist for defective genes are producing their own problems. For example, the test (using polymorphisms) for the defect causing Huntingtons chorea, which causes incurable and rapidly progressive mental deterioration in middle age. Should those at risk be tested for such conditions? Should they have the right to decide whether or not to be tested?

As more such tests become available, they will affect far more people. For example, many millions could be affected by tests to determine their degree of susceptibility to cancer or heart disease. Should employers, insurance companies, building societies or employers be able to ask for such tests? Should they indeed have automatic access to any part of any human genome or should it be the individual's private property? Should children's genomes be considered their property or their parents' property? Are there any conditions in which children should be denied access to gene therapy? Will potential marriage partners ask for print-outs of each other's genomes?

In the end those who decide to keep their genes private will probably lose out financially, because financial institutions will conclude that the most likely reasons for doing so is that there is something to hide, and will react accordingly by refusing mortgages, loans, policies etc. Whether genes which are not just mildly disadvantageous but actively harmful should be regarded as private property, and whether people should have the ability to spread such genes by producing children, are other questions. When deleterious genes can be identified as routinely as infectious diseases can today, there may an be argument for making the genes, too, notifiable. The difference from the patient's point of view is, of course, that for reproductive purposes bad genes are incurable. A woman will marry a man with pneumonia or even syphilis once he has recovered from it. But will she marry a man with six out of seven bad genes for coronary heart disease?

That brings me on to the second form of potential gene therapy, germ line gene therapy. Clearly attitudes to humans and to plants and animals differ greatly. Doctors are preparing for somatic gene therapy for humans but condemning germ line therapy. But no-one is bothering to insert genes into animals or plants on a one-off somatic basis. The effort is going into inserting the genes for pest resistance or drought resistance or leaner meat or whatever into the germ line, into fertilized egg cells, so the genes go not just into one generation but into all the descendants of the animals that grow from the eggs.

Why not do likewise for humans? The qualities we are adding to farm animals and crop plants are those which benefit us, not the animals (though by making the animals more valuable they may benefit them too.) But why not select qualities equally valuable to humans, and set about implanting them into as many people as possible? If disease-resistant chickens and bigger, stronger mice can be produced, why not bigger, stronger disease-resistant humans?

The Fifth Summit Conference on Bioethics, held in Toronto in June 1988, discussed gene therapy and concluded that, while somatic gene therapy only needed the same controls as other new therapies, germ line therapy should not be considered at all. The argument was that it constitutes interference with the genomes of those yet unborn, without their consent, and of a kind which could not be rescinded if it later proved undesirable. The European Medical Research Councils have taken the same line. In 1988 they declared jointly that inserting genes in the human germ line should not be contemplated.

The editorial on gene therapy in the *Lancet* quoted earlier disagrees. 'Why not?' it says. 'How different are decisions that parents now take that affect their offspring to those that involve inserting genes into the germ line? Women choose the fathers of their children. They may choose to do so knowing that they have a high chance of having a genetic defect. If mothers have the right to bear children with AIDS, why can they not choose to have a genetic defect corrected and so not to pass it on to their children?'

One argument against germ line therapy, put forward by leading experts on genetic defects, is to try to prove that it is unnecessary. There is an alternative way to avoid harmful genes being passed on. This is to remove a number of eggs from a woman at risk of giving birth to an affected child, fertilize all the eggs, let them grow to the 8-cell embryo stage and then take one cell from each embryo for DNA testing. Only the embryo or embryos that carry no defects is then reimplanted to develop and be born. The rest are disposed of.

This has already been tested and shown to work in monkeys and will certainly work for humans too. It is much simpler than injecting corrective genes into eggs with defects, and carries no risk of side effects. And it has the effect that germ line gene therapy, injecting genes, would be trying to achieve. It ensures that only healthy babies without genetic defects are born.

As it comes into use over the next few years this technique, developed at the Hammersmith Hospital in London, will undoubtedly do much to ensure more germ lines are free of genetic defects. However, it will not be acceptable to those who forbid abortion. The procedures involved are unnatural and carry a high risk of failure. The mother-to-be is required to undergo the removal of eggs under anaesthetic and for the eggs to be fertilized outside the body and reimplanted. On average only about one in ten reimplanted embryos grow into babies.

Techniques for trying to cure genetic disease by adding genes to egg cells or very early embryos outside the body can perhaps be discounted. They will be unattractive because they involve surgery, as well as being frowned upon. But eventually someone will develop a technique for targetting genes to the ovary and testis and so to the cells which make sperm and eggs. The technique will be tested and shown to work in animals, perhaps put to work routinely in farm animals, until it is nearly one hundred per cent reliable and side-effect-free. Then there is bound to be a demand to make it available for women too. An injection with a harmless retrovirus, targetted to the ovaries and primed with the correct version of a defective gene, followed by normal sex and normal birth, will surely be a very attractive alternative to laparotomies, foetal tests and abortions, in vitro fertilization, and all the rest of the painful, humiliating and passion-killing procedures.

In the foreseeable future it will probably not be possible to delete defective genes before adding correct ones. So the egg cells treated in this way will still be abnormal, with an extra gene squeezed in on an abnormal position on a chromosome. But research has shown that many genes are quite amenable to such treatment and work happily in their new surroundings. As such treatments are improved – with agricultural animal work always showing the way – it will surely soon reach the point where the demand for it in humans cannot be resisted, especially, for some, because it avoids the need for abortion.

Meanwhile, as techniques for implanting genes advance, understanding of how genes control human qualities will advance too. Already mental illnesses such as schizophrenia and manic depression, heart disease, cancer and rheumatoid arthritis are being shown partially to be caused by genetic factors, and research is beginning to suggest new ways to prevent them. Sooner or later we shall discover how genes predispose people towards intelligence and then begin to see how to ensure, in one way or another, that people possess such genes.

Good genes may then be ensured either by an intelligent couple choosing to marry, or by a woman choosing to be inseminated by the frozen sperm of a genius, or by a woman receiving a donor egg or embryo, or by the right genes being targetted to her ovaries by a retrovirus, or by the genes being injected into her egg cell outside her body. Or, more likely by some other means still to come. But what is certain is, that new ways to insert the genes will be found as the genes for qualities like intelligence are identified, and that people will want to improve their children and grandchildren's prospects in the world by pepping up their genes, just as they have always wanted to by other means.

We shall soon have to start to prepare our children, if not ourselves, to make democratic decisions about how to use and regulate genetic engineering not only to cure disease but to produce what is traditionally known as a 'good constitution', i.e., resistance to infectious diseases generally, and to cancer, heart disease, rheumatism, schizophrenia, manic depressive illness and, late in life, Alzheimers disease and Parkinsons syndrome. People will request as a right, and be provided at a price, with the opportunity to select genes for their children and so determine their futures. After good health, sooner or later genes for intelligence and beauty will be on offer.

Genetic engineering is already only one way among several to achieve such ends. Women can already become the recipients of donor eggs or embryos so as to avoid completely the legacy of their own or their husband's genes. The combination of donor eggs with genetic engineering will give parents in fifty years or so a pretty free hand to determine their children's genetic characteristics, if they so wish – and if they can afford it. Perhaps the hardest choices that will have to be made will be which of the potential benefits of genetic engineering and allied techniques should be made available to all in routine medical care, and which should be considered luxuries that the individual has to pay for wholly out of his own pocket.

The power to reshape ourselves and to shape our children and our children's children is coming fast. Above all, we should not be afraid of it. We should grasp it eagerly, making free and informed choices as to how to use it, within the limits of what a free democratic society deems right and proper.

The first human gene therapy experiment has already taken place. It wasn't an attempt to cure a disease, but a means of improving a form of lymphokine therapy described in the chapter on 'Recruiting Natural Killers'. Dr Steven Rosenberg is treating advanced skin cancer, melanoma, which has spread to other parts of the body with tumour-attacking white blood cells. These were removed from tumours and treated outside the body with lymphokines to make them more aggressive. Some of these cells were given added genes before reinfusing them into the cancer patient's body. The added genes were used as markers to follow the movements of the cells.

The aim is to see which types of cells are most effective in attacking tumours. Although most agree with the researchers involved that this is a modest and safe first step toward gene therapy, which can only do good, a decision on whether to permit it was delayed twice by the Recombinant DNA Advisory Committee at the US National Institutes of Health. In February this year Jeremy Rifkin, the well-known American activist against genetic engineering, filed a lawsuit to try to delay it further. Although the experiment went ahead, Rifkind claimed a 'moral' victory. He won the concession that all future human genetic engineering experiments must be publicly discussed and approved before proceeding. This benevolent-sounding formula could lead to endless delays in medical advances.

The gulf between those who support and those who are increasingly opposed to the use of genetic engineering to diagnose and treat human genetic diseases is already widening ominously. In April this year the Head of Scientific Research for the European Community, the Italian Christian Democrat Filippo Maria Pandolfi, ordered a hold on plans for research into the genetic causes of illness until the ethical implications of the work have been further considered. He is reported as saying that he is concerned that the work could lead to what a spokesman called 'genetic manipulation using human tissue'. Pandolfi's Catholicism is thought to have influenced his decision because of the growing number of abortions which this type of research is bound to lead to.

If the programme which was brought to a halt is resumed it will involve the setting up of centres in Paris and London which will supply research laboratories in member countries with DNA from sixty families affected by inherited genetic defects and with a number of DNA probes for use in experimental pre-natal diagnosis. The London centre will be responsible for developing and supplying the probes. The whole thrust will be towards developing more and better pre-natal tests for more genetic diseases with the aim of reducing the risk of affected babies being born, reducing the incidence of genetic disease in the population at large, and developing treatments for those who are born affected by genetic diseases.

There is also concern that gene therapy used to try to cure genetic disease in a single person might lead on to germ line gene therapy in which attempts might be made to insert new genes into reproductive cells so as to affect future generations, though scientists involved in the project which has been halted are emphatic that there is no such intention.

Opposition to EEC work on the Human Genome also comes from the West German Green movement, who have adopted a very aggressive attitude towards scientists investigating human genes, to the point where such research in West Germany is now much reduced.

10

What Being Human Is – The Human Genome Project

About two thousand scientists and technologists in several countries are going to spend the next fourteen years working to understand what being human is. The aim is to map the whole human genome – the complete blueprint for building a man or women – in precise detail down to the last atom.

The Human Genome Project is based in the USA, in the National Institutes of Health. They have been awarded 28 million dollars to fund it during the fiscal year starting 1989. They are hoping and planning for 100 million dollars annually thereafter until the mapping is completed around 2005 AD. The original dream of celebrating the millenium with the complete print out of a human blueprint is now seen as hopelessly ambitious.

The task is formidable. A human genome comprises all the DNA in any one of the thousands of millions of cells in a person's body. Each cell contains the same DNA, though only a small amount of it is active and being transcribed at any time in any one cell, with different genes being activated at different times in different cells according to the cells' functions. The immensely long molecules of DNA are made up of just four different chemical groups called bases; adenine, guanine, cytosine and thymine. It is the order in which these four bases are arranged down the length of a DNA molecule which determines the corresponding order of the amino acids forming the links in long-chain protein molecules, assembled according to DNA's instructions.

The DNA in the nucleus of a cell takes the form of two strands twisted around each other in the famous double spiral. When it is time for a gene's product to be made, the spiral untwists so that a copy can be made of part of one strand, the part which is the gene involved. The copy is sent out into the cell to be transcribed into the protein it is the blueprint for.

The DNA in the nucleus of a human cell is not arranged in one long, double strand. Instead, there are twenty-three pairs of chromosomes (microscopic rods which are reproduced every time a cell divides), each comprising thousands of genes. All the genetic information in DNA is duplicated. Each gene is found in each member of one pair of chromosomes (with the exception of sperms and eggs, which have only one of each gene, so as to form new pairs of genes, one from each parent, when an egg is fertilized). At least, genes are normally paired, when one is missing it causes problems.

If all the DNA in all twenty-three chromosomes, i.e. all the genetic material which is duplicated in the nucleus of every cell in a human being, were pulled out and laid in a straight line it would be six feet long. The DNA from one single chromosome would be several inches long. The twenty-three chromosomes contain very roughly 100,000 genes. The number could be several thousand less or more, it is only an estimate. But some idea of the number of genes needed to make a person has been obtained by looking at the few small sections of chromosomes which have been completely mapped, and seeing how many genes there are per length of DNA. For example, one bit of chromosome – number eleven – which is mapped in detail contains 65,000 bases and five genes.

A total human genome, comprising all the DNA in twenty-three chromosomes in one cell's nucleus, contains about three thousand million bases, or pairs of bases if you count both strands of the double spiral of DNA. If these were written out with simple letters representing each base, they would make two hundred thousand pages of text, thirteen complete sets of the Encyclopaedia Britannica. Embedded in this DNA are the genes, most of them comprising at least 1,200 base pairs from end to end.

But only a relatively small amount of human DNA is actually made up of genes, perhaps three or four per cent of it. In between the successive sequences of a thousand or so bases apiece which form the genes, are several thousand bases of what has been named 'Spacer' DNA, because it carries no message and has no known function, beyond keeping genes apart.

Even within genes, between the sequences of DNA which form parts of the genetic blueprint, are sequences which carry no message. These sequences are called introns. Big genes have over fifty introns scattered through them. When a gene is to be expressed, and the double spiral untwists so that one strand of DNA can be copied to make a single strand of messenger RNA, the introns are neatly cut out of the RNA before it gets to the ribosome where it is transcribed into protein. Some genes are at least 90 per cent introns.

What are introns for? No one yet knows. One theory is that they are a useful help to evolution, by producing a wider variety of proteins – different cell components for natural selection to work on. When the introns are cut out of a messenger there is always a chance that the *exons* – as the meaningful sequences on each side of an intron are called – will join up wrongly, so that the codes for making proteins are reshuffled. The effect of this could be to keep throwing up new shapes of proteins, which might occasionally be valuable to the organism gaining them, though most such reshuffling would be harmful. But that is no more than a theory.

You can see that, what with spacer DNA and introns, only a small proportion of human DNA is meaningful, and in fact it's even smaller than that. For dotted around the genes are large numbers of what are called *pseudogenes*, pseudo because they do have meaningful sequences of DNA representing the blueprints for making proteins, but they have lost the extra sequences needed for transcription. When a gene is copied and its messenger travels to a ribosome, the messenger acquires 'top' and 'tail' sequences. These sequences tell the ribosome to start and stop transcribing. Lacking them, pseudogenes can't be transcribed. But although they have no function they go travelling on from generation to generation, because evolution has no way of getting rid of useless DNA.

(That's looking at it from our point of view. But if we regard pseudogenes as living organisms, a title they have nearly as much right to as do viruses, it is perhaps not surprising that no way of getting rid of them has evolved. Evolution is about serving the needs of genes rather than serving the needs of you and me. That being so, pseudogenes have as much right to perpetuate their existence as active genes. From the pseudogenes' point of view, humans are useful breeding grounds and protectors.)

Clearly mapping human DNA completely is not only a mammoth task but one in which most of the time is going to be spent plodding through the barren, meaningless sequences of spacer DNA, introns and pseudogenes.

The work involved is also exceedingly boring and monotonous. Technicians employed full time on gene sequencing have a very high rate of job turnover. However the team planning the human genome project, a committee of twelve eminent biologists in the USA, have no intention of simply starting at one end of a batch of human DNA and working through to the other end.

While the ultimate target is indeed to know the precise position of every single one of the three thousand million or so bases in human DNA, the project has begun with a lot of work on other, simpler genomes, such as those of *Eschericia coli* (the bacterium used for most human gene cloning experiments), yeasts, worms, fruit flies (because so much work in classical genetics has been done using fruit flies) and pehaps mice. Some genes in these creatures are much better understood than human genes because so much research has been done on them. Because many genes are the same or very similar in all organisms, fruit flies and bacteria will provide a lot of information about human genetics.

Professor Jim Watson, who with Dr Francis Crick first showed how DNA carries genetic blueprints, heads the new Office for Human Genome Research in the USA. Jim Watson describes the project's objective as being, 'To find out what being human is.' The Program Advisory Committee appointed to define the project met for the first time in January 1989 and the programme is still being planned. But it's already clear that, as well as taking in sequencing of organisms other than humans, the project will

begin by mapping the human genome at a coarse, low-defini-
tion level. It will first establish where important genes are on
chromosomes and how DNA is packaged into the chromosomes
before getting down to fine detail.

Jim Watson believes that within five years a map of all the
human chromosomes can be achieved. It will show not only on
which chromosomes many, perhaps most, genes lie, but also
precisely where on the chromosomes the genes are located.

While this large-scale map is being produced, the other half of
the first stage of the project will concentrate on speeding up DNA
sequencing by automating it. The Japanese, with their genius
for automation and technological ingenuity, have been leaders
in this field. In 1987 the Japanese goal was to be able to
sequence one million bases a day by 1990. At present the limit is
10,000 a day. As the problems involved have become more
apparent Japanese scientists have pulled back their expec-
tations to a more modest target of 100,000 bases a day 'within a
few years'.

While automation can undoubtedly speed up sequencing –
besides making it much less boring – there are cautions from
those who should know best, scientists who hold today's records
for gene sequencing. Dr Bart Barrell and his group in the
Cambridge Molecular Biology Laboratory have recently (January 1989) sequenced the entire genome of the biggest virus to be
sequenced to date – cytomegalovirus – 270,000 bases long.
Ellson Chen of Genentech and his team have sequenced the
human growth hormone gene, the longest stretch of human DNA
yet to be sequenced at 70,000 bases.

Both groups did it by hand. They found that automated
sequencing machines lack the accuracy needed for lengthy
sequencing. Sequencing, says Barrell, (quoted in *Science* 2
December 1988) 'is still an art. There are many failures and a lot
of down time.' Both he and Chen say finishing a sequence can
be specially tricky. Barrell says 'It can take as long to get the last
one or two per cent as it took to get all the rest.'

At Barrell's and Chen's sequencing speed, today's state of the
art, it would take one person 30,000 years or two thousand
people fifteen years to sequence all 3000 million bases in the
human genome. And then the task would have to be repeated
several times over in checks to ensure accuracy. Clearly at the
start of the human genome project it's as important to find better

ways to automate gene sequencing as it is to start to sequence genes. It's logical not to devote too much effort to all-out, end-to-end sequencing until the technology to do it quicker has been developed.

In an ideal world this project would lend itself perfectly to international co-operation. With twenty-three pairs of chromosomes, each one easy to sub-divide into regions, what could be more sensible than to carve up the genome, handing over whole chromosomes or bits to different nations and laboratories according to their national needs, particular skills and technical and financial resources? To some extent it's happening. Japan has a national programme to map (place the genes in) and sequence (identify the bases in) the whole of chromosome number 21. Italy is planning to map and sequence the X-chromosome (one of the pairs of sex chromosomes, the only pair that differ between male and female. Men have one X and one smaller and slightly different Y chromosome in their pair of sex chromosomes. Women have two identical X chromosomes.)

The European Community has embarked on a joint programme sequencing a number of smallish genomes including those of *E. coli*, yeast and some viruses. As with the United States' programme, the Community's aim is to learn not only about genes used commercially in biotechnology but also about the human genome, by studying much simpler genomes containing many genes very like our own.

However there are fears that the American research team, with the most money to spare and a co-ordinated national strategy, may not be prepared to give up medically strategic areas of the human genome to European or Japanese labs to sequence. American labs are already trying to patent sequences containing genes for muscular dystrophy and cystic fibrosis. The Soviet Union announced its own programme last year and has given it high priority. It has broad aims and, as yet, there are no offers to co-operate with other labs, though this may change. Smaller, especially developing nations are understandably concerned that knowledge of the human genome, with all its immense potential for understanding, diagnosing, preventing and curing diseases of all kinds, may become increasingly the intellectual property of a few rich nations.

Even within the USA the committee running the human genome project has not yet found a formula to compel the laboratories it is funding to share their data. The brief history of molecular genetics has been one of increasingly intense competition in identifying the genes which are defective in such conditions as muscular dystrophy and cystic fibrosis. One of the first provisos of the Human Genome Project should be clearly stated safeguards to ensure that data concerning human DNA sequences of value to research in tropical diseases is made *freely* available to developing countries.

Well before the human genome is deciphered, humans and now other organisms are already being genetically fingerprinted. In 1984 Professor Alec Jeffreys of Leicester University discovered a sequence of DNA which varies greatly between different individuals. The sequence is repeated at intervals along the individual's DNA and what varies is the number of repeats. The variations in the number of repetitions of the sequence have proved to be an immensely specific and powerful means of identifying individuals, and DNA fingerprinting, as it is called, has been commercialised by ICI's subsidiary Cellmark Diagnostics. Its applications include many forensic investigations, when criminals can be pinpointed from among a number of suspects by their genetic fingerprints, taken from blood at the scene of a crime, and proving or disproving 'blood' relationships claimed by immigrants. Genetic fingerprinting has been further refined by the use of Polymerase Chain Reaction, PCR, in which a sequence of enzymes is used to copy a chosen sequence of DNA millions of times over. This now allows a field of suspects to be narrowed down from the evidence provided by DNA from a single hair left at the scene of a crime. Very recently the same technique has been used by three London hospitals to diagnose the recurrence of cancer and to monitor its treatment, by detecting genetic abnormalities present only in cancer cells and undetectable by any other method. This may ultimately prove even more important than the forensic and familial applications of genetic fingerprinting and PCR.

11

BIOSENSORS:
THE CHEMICAL CANARIES

A huge growth area created by antibodies and enzymes is the making of biosensors. Biosensors use 'living' molecules – enzymes or antibodies – to detect and measure chemicals ranging from glucose in the blood to nerve gases on the battle field. Enzymes are the natural catalysts which promote reactions in living cells. By using detectors borrowed from living things, biosensors are much more sensitive and precise than conventional sensors, just as lymphokines are more potent than ordinary drugs.

Biosensors are due to revolutionize medical diagnosis in the same way and on the same time-scale that lymphokines are going to revolutionize medical treatment. Biosensors belong in this book about genetic engineering not only because the antibodies and enzymes used in them can't be made without it, but also because genetic engineers will improve their sensitivity and so sharpen up biosenses for tomorrow's biosensors.

The fact that an antibody reacts very strongly with a single antigen and an enzyme does the same with a single substrate means that an antibody or an enzyme can be used to detect their opposite number, the antigen or substrate they react with, with amazing precision and in minute quantities. The presence of a single molecule of an antigen or a substrate can be detected by a biosensor using an antibody or an enzyme. The reaction between antibody and antigen or enzyme and substrate involves a chemi-

113

cal change which in turn involves a change in electrical charge, which can be picked up as a current, greatly amplified and then used to sound an alarm, move a needle on a meter, record a magnetic trace in a computer's memory, alter a digital read-out, or do anything else needed to make whoever is using the biosensors aware that it has sensed what it is there to sense.

But the existence of such reactions was of no practical use until the coming of genetic engineering made it possible to mass-produce enzymes and antibodies to order, by cloning the genes for them. Now any required enzyme or antibody can be produced; enzymes by inserting the gene for the enzyme into a cell culture and cloning it; antibodies by injecting the appropriate antigen into a mouse and immortalizing the cells making an antibody against the antigen. In this way the sharp ends of biosensors, the parts that actually do the sensing, can be mass-produced, by the invincible partnership of genetic engineering and monoclonal antibodies.

Biosensors have opened up a wide range of exciting possibilities for scientists, doctors and engineers. For patients as well as doctors there are now coming into being cheap, simple, use-once-and-throw-away little pocket-pen sized gadgets to keep in the bathroom cupboard and use to test a sample of urine or saliva when someone wants to know if he has flu or just a hangover, or when to try to conceive a baby, or when diabetics need an injection of insulin.

Biosensors for diabetics, which use enzymes which react with glucose to measure blood sugar levels, are now in use. Future models will directly control the flow of insulin into a diabetic's bloodstream, measuring his needs from moment to moment and feeding the findings to a microprocessor implanted in the body. This will in turn control the rate of release of insulin from supplies also implanted in the body. Such a set-up will mimic the natural working of the insulin-supplying organ, the pancreas, much better than anything available today and so improve the quality of life for diabetics. The same sort of system will soon be used to control the delivery of chemotherapy to treat cancer.

Biosensors are being put to work first in medicine, but there are many uses for them in other areas too. Detectors for toxic or explosive gases in mines and tunnels, replacing the canaries miners used to carry with 'chemical canaries', will soon be on the market. Other biosensors are likely soon to keep watch for traces of chemicals or micro-organisms polluting water supplies. They could be used by military or security forces to detect nerve gases or hidden bombs. They can monitor the environment for traces of pesticides or herbicides. They can control greenhouse horticulture by measuring levels of nutrients in soil or water and adjusting supplies of nutrients to constant levels.

Through his work on the liquefaction of coal, Dr John Colby at Sunderland Polytechnic is finding new uses for enzymes made by genetic engineering as biosensors for poisonous gas. Coal in seams too awkward and expensive to mine normally is sometimes extracted by pumping hot air and steam into the seams to vapourize the organic chemicals in the coal, which are then collected and condensed at the surface. A major problem is that the process also releases a lot of odourless, tasteless deadly carbon monoxide – the gas that miners' canaries were originally taken down mines to give warning of.

Dr Colby and Dr Edwin Williams of Newcastle University have found enzymes in bacteria able to detect carbon monoxide at levels twenty times lower than any other detector can manage. Carbon monoxide biosensors made by John Colby change colour when the bacterial enzyme reacts with minute traces of carbon monoxide. The reaction can be used to set off an alarm.

Outside mines another use for this biosensor could be in nuclear submarines, where carbon monoxide can insidiously build up to dangerous levels over months spent submerged. Another idea is to use the enzyme as a filter in cigarettes, to remove the carbon monoxide produced by burning tobacco, which helps to cause heart disease and is one of the several health hazards of smoking. If enough enzyme is present it can both detect the presence of and eliminate carbon monoxide. But why not – suggests Colby, only half in jest – instead build the gene for the bacterial enzyme into the tobacco plant? And add a heat switch so that when a pipe or cigarette is lit the enzyme, made naturally by the growing plant, is activated and destroys the carbon monoxide? All the tricks needed already exist; ways to put genes into tobacco plants, heat switches and now the enzyme needed.

It was the invincible duo, genetic engineering and monoclonal antibodies, which mass-produced enzymes and antibodies to order and made biosensors a realistic proposition. But before they could become a commercial reality another problem had to be overcome. Life had to be linked to non-life. Enzyme or antibody molecules had to work as one with electrodes and silicon chips in order to translate the work of the enzyme into an electronic warning signal.

The first steps towards this, as in some other areas of biotechnology, were held up because they involved scientists of different sorts who had never met getting to know each other. As one of the pioneers of biosensor design, Professor John Albery of Imperial College London puts it, when the first attempts to pick up an electric current from an antibody-antigen or enzyme-substrate reaction were made, 'The biochemists complained that the electrodes used by electrochemists destroyed their beautiful biological molecules. The biological molecule would just go SPLUT on the electrode. The electrochemist would say to the biochemist, "Your horrible protein molecule has poisoned my high-tech electrode." The biochemist would reply, "Your horrible electrode has destroyed my beautiful biological molecule."

That was how it was five years ago. Now, through the work of John Albery and others like him, enzymes and antibodies have been conned into thinking, so to speak, that the electrode they touch, the non-living surface that is the start of the electronic circuitry they feed into, is really living material. Life and non-life have been made compatible. The ultimate consequences of that are immeasurable. More of them later.

The ability to pick up tiny, tell-tale electric currents from biological systems at work is already being exploited in biosensors which measure blood sugar for diabetics, and urea for people using artificial kidney machines. These substances react with enzymes. The first generation of biosensors exploits enzymes. The second generation will make use of antibodies, which can be perhaps one million times more sensitive than enzymes.

The ability of an antibody-based biosensor to react with just one antigen produced by just one disease organism will allow simple, infallible, rapid and cheap diagnosis of infectious diseases, with profound social consequences. There will be much less reliance on central laboratories. At first a doctor or nurse, later (as biosensors become more and more widely available and reliable), the patient him or herself, will be able to get results in a GP's surgery within a few moments, from tests which today take weeks for a central laboratory to produce. The output from the biosensors will soon be linked directly to computers programmed with expert systems to aid diagnosis in the GP's surgery. Power will shift irrevocably away from the hospital to the GP.

Later it will shift increasingly to the patient. As home computing progresses, as interest in personal health care grows, health care itself, responsibility for diagnosis, eventually responsibility for treatment will shift more and more to the patient. A well-programmed home computer and battery of bathroom cupboard biosensors will do away with the need for most visits to a doctor.

Scientists are now getting very good at interfacing (linking up) biological molecules and micro-electronic systems. While the first uses for such interfacing involve biosensors, they are only the threshold of a new world in which the distinction between life and non-life is going steadily to disappear. For example artificial limbs controlled directly by the brain will pick up tiny electrical signals from nerves and amplify and translate them via a microprocessor into a form which a mechanical prosthesis will respond to.

The interface between life and non-life is all-important and messages will travel across it both ways. Nerve impulses will go out across it to drive artificial limbs. Incoming signals from artificial sense organs will cross the interface in the other direction on their way into the brain. Artificial eyes, ears and noses which will actually extend human senses, so we can see in the dark and hear sound only bats can hear today, are real possibilities. Our mental capacities as well as our limbs and our senses will be able to be repaired and extended. Says Dr John Higgins of Cranfield Institute of Technology, another world leader in the development of biosensors, 'If we become able to control artificial limbs by signals from the brain, then it follows that interfacing between neurones [brain cells] and computers at the mental level may become possible too.' We may eventually put silicon chips into our brains as well as into our bodies so as to repair damage and replace broken parts.

The growing invasion of our brains and bodies by electronic components, with appropriate interfaces between chips and neurones to repair brain damage and control prostheses, will be countered by another invasion – that of the metal world by the living world. As the boundary between life and non-life blurs and disappears, life will move outwards as well as non-life inwards. Protein molecules which have the complexity needed to act as electronic components are being developed as alternatives to silicon and gallium arsenide components.

Harwell scientists, who are designing biosensors which use antibodies as the sensing molecules, see their work as a step towards biological computers. The biosensors require the interactions of single molecules, one antibody with one antigen molecule. If the antibody is embedded in a membrane one or two molecules thick then, when an antigen molecule binds to an antibody molecule, that binding distorts the entire membrane. If an electrical current passes through the membrane, the binding of a single molecule will alter the current.

This is very like what happens inside the brain when we learn something new. Chemicals passing from one brain cell to another alter the membrane separating the two cells. The effect is to make the cells communicate more easily. The sum total of many millions of such effects happening over large areas of the brain is a new memory. Could computers be built which stored information by single-molecule, protein-protein reactions distorting membranes and facilitating the passage of currents like those between brain cells?

The great advantage of such a computer memory would be that it would take up hundreds of times less room than even the smallest silicon chips. The important thing with computers is to make them as small as possible, so the electrical current has less distance to travel and they work faster. So biological memory systems are immediately attractive. They will need to use molecule-to-molecule interactions which combine the precision of antibody-antigen reactions with the ability to release the molecule which is being reacted with very swiftly – an ability possessed by enzymes. This will give the system the on-off switching capacity needed by electronic components. (Bio-electronic components could be made as antibodies – see 'Greening Industry').

The idea of making new electronic components out of biological molecules has been around for a few years. But it has really only begun to be seriously researched in the past year or two. Using genetic and protein engineering, it is possible to make protein molecules with electrical properties similar to those of rectifiers, condensers and so on, and to link them up with other electrically-conducting organic molecules.

Biological systems for collecting and passing electric currents around already exist in nature. In chloroplasts, which trap the sun's energy and use it to build new plant material, and in mitochrondria, which store the energy derived from the breakdown of sugars with oxygen in compact, energy-rich molecules. In both chloroplasts and mitochrondria, electrical currents flow along paths defined by the structures of complex protein molecules. Both chloroplasts and mitochondria probably evolved from free-living one-celled organisms to become parts of our bodies. Could they be re-evolved to repair damaged bodies? Certainly we can learn from them. Building circuitry of their 'living' kind into advanced biosensors, intelligent prostheses, or 'biochips' to repair damaged brains, could do away with the problem of compatibility.

Since it is now possible to pick up currents coming out of enzymes, antibodies and other biological molecules, it must also be possible to feed power into them. This has indeed been done, opening up the intriguing possibility of switching living processes on and off. Such processes as photosynthesis in chloroplasts and respiration in mitochrondria, involve sequences of several enzymes, linked together and very precisely arranged, like a sequence of machine tools on a production line. Biotechnologists hope to lift out complete sequences of such enzymes and to use them in medicine or industry or biosensing. It may be possible to clone complete sequences of such enzymes by inserting all the genes together into cell cultures.

These molecular machine tools need power, power in the familiar sense of electric power. A stream of electrons – an electric current – is fed to a system of linked enzymes in chloroplasts and mitochrondria – and they use, by the standards of the living cell, a lot of it. The current is fed in via a sort of biological electric plug, a molecule called Cytochrome C, which plugs neatly into the end of an enzyme molecule and feeds electrons into it.

Take the enzymes out of the cell, or clone them on their own, and they are disconnected. They lack power. But Dr Allen Hill, of the Inorganic Chemistry Department of Oxford University has found a way to plug a power supply in to enzymes. He uses enzymes taken out of cells with Cytochrome C plugs stuck into them. An electrode, a charged terminal pushing out a stream of electrons, is dipped into a solution of the enzymes. Dr Hill has found how to carry current from the electrode into the enzymes via their Cytochrome C plugs. It's done by adding ions, positively-charged magnesium and calcium atoms, to the solution. The ions ferry electrons across the electrode to the Cytochrome C molecules. Ultimately, such a system could be used to power up massive arrays of enzymes or abzymes, used for industrial scale synthesis.

119

Besides being potentially compatible with the human body and with all forms of life, and capable of endless improvement through protein engineering, biological molecules used in electronic devices will have two further advantages. They have the complexity needed to allow really advanced functions. It is doubtful if a machine built out of simpler molecules than proteins could ever think in the complex ways that the human brain achieves. And they will be biodegradeable. An outdated biological computer could give its programmers a good meal or enrich their compost heaps. It could grow new parts to order, and even reproduce itself if its parts were built according to DNA blueprints.

So protein engineers will soon be drawing up the genetic blueprints for micro-electronic components and biosensors for use inside and outside the human body and elsewhere. In fact they are probably doing so already in laboratories such as those of IBM. Since the complexity of the proteins involved will be their great advantage, the best way to make them will probably be to clone them. Much of tomorrow's computing power will be born in bioreactors.

It seems to me not only possible but to be welcomed that as the greening of industry proceeds, as we become more responsible for our health with our biosensors linked to our expert systems on our home computers, as those computers themselves become more like soft flesh and blood and less like hard metal, that our houses will go the same way and that we shall end up growing our houses as enthusiastically as we grow our gardens today. Cell cultures will be genetically programmed to grow into our fridges, cookers, freezers, beds, tables, chairs. . . . Imagine a table of living wood, a cushion of living fur – which never graced an animal – a carpet of living growing wool. . . . All living in the intelligent house with its central computer deciding when to apply for planning permission to grow the attic and, no doubt, telling the carpet to get its hair cut.

12

THE
GREEN GENES

Plants as well as people can be given new genes and not just genes from plants. All living things speak the same genetic language, no matter how unlike their bodies are. (Some viruses in fact speak a slightly different language, that is their genetic code is made of RNA rather than DNA, perhaps because they are descended from messengers which escaped from the confines of cells. But there are enzymes which naturally translate RNA into DNA in living cells and it is quite easy to use them to translate viral RNA into DNA.) This means that any gene can be taken from any living organism and inserted into any other organism, where it will work normally. The substance, the protein for which the gene is the blueprint, will be made in accordance with the gene's instructions wherever the gene is inserted. Human genes are already at work in yeast, bacteria, sheep and mice.

In practice it is not quite as simple as that. Genes shifted into a new home, a different organism, may need new sets of instructions added to them to make them express themselves in their new homes. But the extra instructions needed are also being rapidly identified and can be moved from gene to gene as easily as genes to new homes. There is now no real doubt that by tacking on such instructions, or if necessary translating from RNA to DNA, any gene from any living organism can be made to work in any other organism. Ways still have to be found to get the genes safely into some of the new homes where thay are needed. But once there, they'll work all right.

This growing ability to shift working genes from any form of life into any other form of life at present means more to agriculture and especially to plant breeders than it does to any one else. Conventional plant breeding involves first searching for a wild variety of a crop plant species which possesses a wanted characteristic, such as resistance to drought or to virus disease. That search may be long and laborious and it may fail, evolution may not have provided any member of that particular species with the wanted characteristic.

If the search succeeds then the wild plant is crossed with the cultivated plant; pollen from one fertilizes the ova of the other, and the resultant seeds carry genes from both parent plants. That's not the end. Only some of the offspring will have the wanted gene. They will have large numbers of unwanted characteristics bred in from the wild plant. Along with the single, wanted gene there will be thousands of unwanted genes, some of them inferior to the genes of the cultivated plant the wild genes co-exist with or supplant in the offspring of the cross.

Several more generations are needed to breed out, as far as possible, all the unwanted genes while leaving the wanted one in place. After several years work the outcome is an unsatisfactory compromise which, on balance, is better than the breed it replaces.

Contrast this laborious process with the future offered by gene shifting. A single gene conferring a valuable characteristic, say virus resistance, is required. The search for the gene is made not just in the same species as the crop plant which is to be improved, not just among closely related plants, not even just in the plant kingdom but among bacteria, fungi and viruses, even animals if necessary.

Clearly there is a much better chance of finding the wanted gene. When it is found the gene is cloned, multiplied millions of times over in a laboratory cell culture so as to provide plenty of genes ready for implanting. Then the gene is inserted into a single cell taken from the crop plant and the single cell is grown into a whole new plant. That plant and all its descendants, so long as it is propagated vegetatively, that is without sexual reproduction mixing new genes into it and maybe losing others, will possess the resistance to the virus conferred by the gene.

This will have been achieved by selecting the wanted character-istic from the genetic resources of the entire planet. It will have been achieved in one single generation, and without adding in any unwanted genes at all. And of course more than one benefic-ial gene, taken from more than one original host, may be added in one single step, by one single injection of genetic material.

With such immense potential advantages, it is not surprising that plant breeding is seen as the biggest money spinner of all for gene shifters – for the immediate future at least. Independent consul-tants to seed and herbicide companies have estimated that by 2000 AD genetic engineering will be adding 20,000 million dollars to the value of crops worldwide every year. 'I am convinced', says Howard Schneiderman, chief scientist of the Monsanto company, which has invested more resources in genetic engineering than any other private company worldwide, 'that for some major crops resistance to insects and other pests will become available by the 1990s. In some key crops we shall have shifted the central thrust of plant protection from treatment to prevention. The result will be decreased dependence on conventional pesticides. . . Biotechno-logy has the ability to make farming a more reliable and more profitable business, less subject to the whims of the weather and to pests, requiring less chemicals and less fertilizers.'

To see just how far plant breeders have already gone with such experiments, let's look straightaway at one example of the state of the art today, the creation, by a private American genetic engi-neering company, Calgene, of tobacco plants which are resistant to a herbicide. The aim of such experiments is to allow weeds around crops to be eliminated by herbicides without affecting the crop itself.

It is more than unfortunate for the image of genetic engineering that so many such key techniques have been first tested on the tobacco plant, a crop which many would like to see eliminated from the planet because of the harm to health caused by its product. But tobacco is not only a major money-earning crop, it is also one of the few important crops that belong to the great group of plants – dicotyledons – that genetic engineers have already succeeded in inserting new genes into. The other great group of plants, called monocotyledons, is proving much less easy to get genes into. Since nearly all the world's important crops are monocotyledons, this is delaying the advance of genetic engineering into plant breeding and pushing a lot of effort into tobacco.

Ways to get new genes into monocotyledons are being worked on hard in many labs, and may soon succeed, and then the image of plant genetic engineering will undoubtedly improve. For now, like it or not, it's the tobacco plant which is often getting the benefit in projects such as the one which follows.

Three kinds of genes have been found which can make plants resistant to herbicides. One group makes the plant make more of whatever it is that the herbicides destroy, so more herbicide is needed to destroy the plant. The second group change the thing the herbicide destroys – in fact an enzyme – so that the herbicide can no longer destroy it. The third group of protective genes give the plant the ability to detoxify the herbicide, to break it down and render it harmless.

The first two types of protective genes have already been built into one or two crop plants experimentally. The third approach – making plants able to detoxify herbicides – has proved more difficult to achieve. But it is being eagerly pursued, because plants which can detoxify herbicides are more resistant to them than plants made resistant to herbicides in other ways.

Calgene have succeeded in this third approach. They have implanted genes for an enzyme which breaks down a herbicide called Bromoxynil in tobacco plants. Tobacco plants protected in this way were sprayed with eight times more than the highest concentration of Bromoxynil which has ever been used by farmers. The plants were completely unaffected, the enzymes made by their new genes broke down all the herbicide to harmless chemicals. The protective genes are inherited. So after a few years the cost of such genetic engineering will have become infinitesimal compared to the savings it brings about in continuing to increase crop yield.

Resistance to herbicides brought about by genetic engineering may be a mixed blessing. By allowing heavier doses of herbicides to be delivered to weeds, it will increase rather than decrease chemical pollution of the environment – exactly the opposite of the benefits envisaged by Schneiderman. And ways will have to be found to prevent genes for herbicide resistance spreading from crops to weeds of the same species. Wild tobacco plants pose no threat, but when ways are found to insert genes for herbicide resistance into crops with wild relatives that are common weeds, as with some cereals, then there will be real danger of creating new superweeds. Against these risks must be set the added value to farmers and national economies of crops better protected against competition from weeds.

While its application in this case is controversial, the genetic engineering involved shows how sophisticated the craft has become in the last few years. The first step was to search not plants but soil bacteria for strains which might already have evolved a means of protecting themselves against poisonous chemicals. Here, straight away, is an advantage of being able to look beyond the crop plant's own species and even beyond the plant kingdom in search of wanted characteristics. Bacteria reproduce many times faster than plants, and exchange valuable genes among themselves more rapidly still. This meant there was a much better chance of finding the wanted genes for herbicide resistance in soil bacteria than anywhere else.

Sure enough, a bacterium resistant to the herbicide was found. The next step was to find the enzyme which breaks down the herbicide, and then to work out the exact structure, the DNA sequence of the gene for the enzyme, from the corresponding sequence of the amino acids in the enzyme molecule. Then, knowing its exact structure scientists were able to search for and identify the gene itself in the bacteria.

Next a way had to be found to insert the gene into a tobacco plant. It was essential that the gene should be inserted into every cell of the plant, in order that it would be found in the chloroplasts – the green photosynthesizing granules – where the herbicide would normally kill the plant by preventing photosynthesis. The gene had to be present in chloroplasts so that the herbicide-destroying enzyme would be made there, where it was needed. Another reason why the gene had to be put into every cell of the plant was so that it would find its way into the pollen or ova they produced, so that resistance to herbicides would be passed on to future generations.

This meant implanting the gene into a single cell from which all the other cells in the plant would then be derived by cell division. In an animal this can only be done by implanting the gene into a fertilized egg cell. But some plants, including the tobacco plant, can be grown from a single cell taken from a mass of cells grown in turn from a bit of stem, root or leaf. The gene for herbicide resistance had to be implanted into such a cell with precision and integrated into the cell's DNA so that the added gene would be duplicated and passed on with the plant's own genes at every successive cell division.

All this was achieved by using a second bacterium, in addition to the one which donated the wanted gene. This second bacterium is called *Agrobacterium tumefaciens*. As its name suggests, *Agrobacterium* has the ability to cause a sort of cancer in the plant it infects. It does this by inserting its own genes into the nuclei of the cells of the plants it infects, in such a way that the bacterium's genes actually become indistinguishable from the plant's own genes.

The bacterial genes then make the cells containing them grow uncontrollably, like human cancer cells. So the plant forms a big lumpy tumour-like growth in which the bacteria can grow and flourish. By inserting other genes into *Agrobacterium* these genes can be inserted in amongst the plant's own genes too. This behaviour makes *Agrobacterium* an ideal tool for plant genetic engineers, and it is now being more and more widely used to get new genes into plants.

But before *Agrobacterium* could be used to insert the gene for herbicide resistance into tobacco plants, *Agrobacterium* itself had to be altered by genetic engineering so as to render it harmless, unable to cause the formation of 'tumours', but still able to insert genes into plant DNA. When that had been done, the cloned gene for the herbicide-busting enzyme was inserted into the now-harmless *Agrobacterium*. Then a small piece of living tissue was cut out of the leaf of a tobacco plant and deliberately infected with *Agrobacterium* carrying the added gene. Finally the infected cells were separated and grown individually into plants, every cell of which, when all went well, contained genes for herbicide resistance. It was these plants that were then tested to see if they were resistant to Bromoxynil.

Actually the genetic engineering was a little more complicated even than that. Bromoxynil kills plants by destroying an enzyme vital to photosynthesis. So the protective enzyme which inactivates the herbicide had to be produced in the chlorophyll of the tobacco plant. This meant the gene for making the enzyme had to be made to express itself (i.e. produce the enzyme) in chloroplasts.

Another part of the ever-growing genetic engineering tool kit was used for this – a short sequence of DNA, a promoter, which any gene the promoter is attached to expresses itself, but only in chloroplasts. This promoter was taken from genes which work only in chloroplasts and tacked onto the herbicide-resistance gene before the gene was put into *Agrobacterium*. It did the trick; the herbicide-destroying enzyme was made in the tobacco plant's chloroplasts and they and the plant became virtually invulnerable to Bromoxynil.

So, in order to achieve the wanted resistance to a herbicide, the necessary gene was sought and found in a soil bacterium, cloned and had added to it a sequence to switch it on in the right place, before being inserted into *Agrobacterium*, which itself had first been rendered harmless by more genetic engineering. Only then was the gene inserted into a cell which was grown into a plant with herbicide resistance. That is the advanced state of the art of green plant genetic engineering today.

You may ask why resistance to herbicides in particular has been engineered so rapidly and to such a high degree of sophistication. While commercially valuable, it is not the most valuable property a farmer would wish for in his crop. The answer is that it is the agrochemical companies, the makers of herbicides, who have the most money to spend on genetic engineering. They have perceived that if money can be made by selling their herbicide, even more money can be made if crops can be made resistant to just that one herbicide. The profits to be made from selling genetically-engineered seeds with other valuable properties, on the other hand, are so far relatively low. This is one reason why other, more valuable characteristics are being engineered into crops more slowly than herbicide resistance.

The technique described above involves isolating single cells from leaf tissue which has been infected with *Agrobacterium* carrying the wanted genes, and then growing the cells into new plants. It is much easier to persuade single cells to regenerate into complete plants in some plant species than it is in others. It is still proving very difficult in monocotyledons, the great group of plants to which all cereals and most other major crops belong.

As yet no research team has managed reliably to insert genes into cells from monocotyledons and then to make the cells regenerate into complete plants. Japanese scientists of the Plantech Research Institute in Yokohama have succeeded in creating transgenic rice plants, but no one has yet repeated their experiments.

But geneticists are trying to bypass the need to regenerate plants from single cells. One promising way to do this has been developed at the Max Planck Institute in West Germany. A research team there have injected a solution of genes into the tiny shoots growing from maize plants which later as the plants grow form the reproductive organs, pollen and ova. Pollen from one plant which had been injected with genes was used to fertilize ova from another plant which had been treated in the same way. Just two seeds out of 3000 produced from this cross grew into plants which had incorporated the injected genes into their own genetic material.

It is too early to say whether this technique will make it possible to introduce new genes into cereal crops, such as wheat and barley, as well as maize. The scientists involved are optimistic but some others are doubtful. Other ingenious approaches are being tried. At Imperial College in London, Professor Ken Buck is leading a team investigating viruses, geminiviruses to carry new genes into monocotyledons. Normally these viruses cause serious plant diseases. But Professor Buck's team have rendered their geminivirus harmless, by removing the gene for one of the proteins which form the coat of the virus particles. The virus no longer causes serious disease but is still able to infect cereal plants.

The idea is that the geminivirus, which spreads very rapidly, will spread through an entire plant infecting the reproductive cells along with all the other cells. Because the virus integrates its gene naturally into the genes in the nuclei of the cells it infects, the added genes will be integrated too, ensuring that the added genes are handed on to future generations via the reproductive cells.

Professor Buck's team hope to use geminivirus to create cereals which will go on perpetuating the added gene indefinitely. But they also see it being valuable for use within one single generation. Geminiviruses are so infective that it may be possible to use them, with added genes for pest or herbicide resistance, to infect a whole field of a crop very quickly. Whether such 'one-off' genetic engineering will be economically worthwhile or competitive with the use of genetically engineered seeds remains to be seen.

Other techniques for introducing genes into monocotyledons are being developed. The most sensational, though perhaps not the technique most likely to be adapted on a large scale in the long run, is a sort of shotgun approach in which tiny particles of tungsten coated with DNA are literally blasted into as many cells as possible in a developing plant embryo. The fact that this actually sometimes works says more for the resilience of plant genes than it does for plant biotechnology. Meanwhile, while we wait for the breakthrough needed to insert new genes reliably and cheaply into monocotyledons, we can look at more examples of what is already being achieved by inserting genes into the other great group – the dicotyledons.

We have looked at one example, resistance to herbicides engineered into tobacco plants. Resistance to insect pests will be more valuable in the long term. Dr Vaughan Hilder and Dr Angharad Gatehouse of Durham University, working with the Cambridge Plant Breeding Centre have found a way to insert such genes into plants, though, again, so far only into dicotyledons.

The cow pea plant protects itself against beetles which would otherwise feed on it by producing chemicals which stop the beetles digesting their food. The plant's chemical stops beetles secreting tryspin, the digestive enzyme that normally breaks down plant proteins in the beetles' guts so the proteins can be absorbed. Without trypsin the beetles cannot absorb the proteins they need for life and die within two days.

Vaughan Hilder and Angharad Gatehouse have transferred the cow pea gene for the trypsin inhibitor out of cow peas and put it into tobacco plants, using *Agrobacterium* as the carrier (*Agrobacterium* has become a routine way to shift plant genes around). The tobacco plants treated in this way kill every insect pest which normally preys on tobacco. The good news is that the plants also kill every insect pest which preys on cereals. So, when a reliable way to get genes into cereals is found, this protective gene and many other protective genes, will be waiting cloned and ready to be put into wheat, barley, rice and the rest.

Durham University's Botany Department is one of the world's pioneering centres for plant genetic engineering, and Angharad Gatehouse and her colleagues are looking well beyond the insertion of single genes to protect plants in one way at a time. As potential financial benefits cause labs to focus on plant biochemistry – a hitherto-unfashionable area of research – it is now becoming clear that over many millions of years plants have evolved numerous chemical strategies to defend themselves against pests. Suddenly these are all of great interest because it may be possible to transfer them to crops.

Angharad Gatehouse is identifying the chemicals involved in several such defences. She foresees crop plants being protected by batteries of added genes, several for different pest-repelling chemicals and other genes for extra food value, resistance to virus diseases, herbicide resistance and perhaps even the ability to fix nitrogen from the air, doing away with the need for nitrogenous fertilizers.

A number of plants and shrubs, legumes such as peas and beans, are able to absorb nitrogen from the air and 'fix' it; use it to make new plant material. Nitrogen is an essential constituent of proteins. Nitrogen fixing counters the slow loss of this essential element into the atmosphere as living things die and decay. The first vital step in nitrogen fixing is carried out not by the legumes themselves but by bacteria living in a mutually beneficial, symbiotic relationship with them in protective nodules on the roots and stems of the plants. One of the first targets for genetic engineers has been to identify the genes for the enzymes these bacteria use to fix nitrogen, and to transfer these genes into crop plants, so that the plants could fix nitrogen themselves instead of needing bacteria to do it for them. This would benefit the poorer nations of the world with agriculture-based economies especially, because of the high and ever-growing cost of nitrogen-based fertilizers. These are expensive because a lot of energy is used in their manufacture.

Unfortunately not one but several genes are needed for nitrogen fixing. So far the problems involved in transferring all of them into plant cells in a way which will allow them to do the same job as they do in bacteria have not been overcome. This is not to say they never will be, only that the number of genes and other problems involved makes the creation of nitrogen fixing crops a task for third-generation genetic engineering, when techniques for inserting genes into specific places on chromosomes have been perfected. That is probably several years away, but when it comes it will revolutionize agriculture.

Another Durham University scientist, Dr Charlie Shaw is deploying genes to protect plants in a different way, once again making use of that good friend of plant genetic engineers, *Agrobacterium* You will remember that *Agrobacterium* induces a form of plant cancer in plants which it infects. In order to do so it has to gain access to the plant and it can only do this through some sort of breach in the plant's outer defences. When a plant is wounded, chemicals ooze out of the wound into the soil and are detected by any *Agrobacterium* lurking nearby. As soon as they pick up the scent, so to speak, *Agrobacteria* start to wriggle towards the plant through the soil, always moving to higher and higher concentrations of the tell-tale chemicals leaking from the wounded plant.

Charlie Shaw had the bright idea of using the way in which *Agrobacteria* home in on wounded plants so as to attack them to make the bacteria protect the plants instead. The process where by *Agrobacterium* infects plants and inserts its genes into them is controlled by some of *Agrobacterium's* genes. These genes are 'switched on' when the chemical exuded from a wounded plant which an *Agrobacterium* is homing in on reaches a certain level. This signals that the plant is very near and the bacterium should be getting ready to infect it.

Charlie Shaw and his colleagues have identified the gene switch, the DNA sequence in *Agrobacteria* which activates the genes for invading plants. They have attached this switch instead to other genes, genes taken from other bacteria which make chemicals which attack insect pests. These genes have been inserted into *Agrobacteria*. The product is a bacterium which moves towards wounded plants in response to their chemical signals but which, when it gets close to the plant, produces natural pesticides instead of attacking it.

The plan is to release cultures of such *Agrobacteria* into fields of crops. The natural pesticides would be released when crop plants were damaged. One advantage of this ingenious idea, which is now being developed by ICI's Plant Protection Division working with Dr Shaw's team, is that the natural pesticide is only made when plants are wounded and so at special risk of insect attack. This avoids the waste of resources involved in the alternative genetic engineering approach, in which genes for making natural pesticides are inserted into the crop plants themselves, which then make them continuously. Most of the time plants are probably not under any real threat of attack from insects in the soil, so non-stop pesticide making would divert resources from making more plant material and decrease the value of the crop. Another advantage is that *Agrobacteria* infect both monocotyledons and dicotyledons. So the techniques could be used to protect cereals and other major crops.

13

ANTI-SENSE GENES AND GENETIC TOOLKITS

Genetic engineers plan to make crops invulnerable to disease as well as insect pests. One means could be through the use of Anti-Sense RNA. Using anti-sense RNA is a beautiful idea but it takes a little explaining.

When a virus infects a plant it inserts its own viral genes in among the plant's genes in cell nuclei. Then the virus makes more virus, just as the cell makes more cell components. A viral gene, made of DNA, is copied into the form of RNA, a chemical which differs only slightly from DNA. The copy, known as messenger RNA, is sent out into the cell to the organelles called ribosomes where new proteins, new cell components are made to the instructions of messengers, whether they come from a virus or from the cell's own genes.

When a gene is expressed, that is when its instructions are followed and the cell containing the gene makes new component proteins, enzymes for example, in accordance with the gene's instructions, what happens is this. The gene is in the form of two spirals of DNA wound round each other. The two spirals unwind, exposing their lengths ready to be copied. A strand is copied and the copy is sent out of the nucleus where the genes are stored and travels out into the cell, into the cytoplasm – the region outside the nucleus.

This single strand of RNA, a chemical very like but slightly different from DNA, travels to a ribosome, one of the many organelles in the cytoplasm where the instructions of genes are translated into new proteins, in the process called transcription. RNA is transcribed into protein. The messenger, as the strand of RNA is called, has to be in the form of a single strand, because as a new protein is assembled at the ribosome it is assembled along the length of the RNA molecule, using it as a template.

When a virus infects a plant the virus inserts its own genes into the plant's cells and they order the cells to make messenger RNA copies of them, the viral genes, instead of the cell's own genes. The idea behind the development of anti-sense RNA is to build an extra gene into a plant which will defend it against a particular virus. The extra gene will prevent that virus's messenger ever getting through to the ribosome, so that the virus cannot replicate. A virus which cannot replicate might just as well never have infected a cell.

When the protective gene is copied to make messenger RNA, its message literally cancels out the virus genes messenger's message. The protective gene's sequence of bases is complementary to the viral gene's sequence. Complementary sequences of RNA are attracted to each other. If a strand of messenger RNA from a viral gene on its way to a ribosome to be transcribed into a viral protein meets a strand of complementary RNA from the protective gene then the two will be attracted to each other and will cleave together along their lengths.

Once the single strand of viral messenger RNA has a strand of complementary RNA stuck to it along its length, it can no longer act as a messenger. A messenger has to be a naked single strand in order for it to be transcribed into protein. So the message is smothered, or cancelled out, by an anti-message, a sequence of anti-sense RNA produced as a messenger by the protective gene.

The hope is that crops with such protective genes, with of course neat little control sequences stuck onto the genes to activate them whenever a cell containing them is invaded by a virus, will be able to protect completely against the replication of viruses and so against their harmful effects.

The potential uses for anti-sense genes and anti-sense RNA go beyond plant genetic engineering. They are being seriously considered and researched as a means of protecting humans against AIDS and even against forms of cancer.

The idea of using anti-sense RNA to protect against AIDS is

described in the chapter on AIDS. The idea of using it against cancers is a longer shot. But it is a fact that one essential step in the process that makes cells cancerous often involves oncogenes being expressed in the wrong place or at the wrong time. If means could be found to insert and switch on anti-sense genes to cancel out messengers from oncogenes whenever they threatened to cause trouble, potential cancer patients, or people who had previously had cancer, might be protected against its development.

That idea is being researched seriously, but there are too many ifs and buts in it for it to be more than an idea as yet. But in agriculture where genetic engineers can move faster, anti-sense genes have already been used to good advantage. They have made tomatoes tastier, and produced a tomato sauce which sticks to spaghetti as proper tomato sauce should.

Tomatoes bought in shops in the UK and the USA lack flavour because they are picked when green and treated with ethylene gas to make them turn red. They aren't allowed to ripen on the plant because that makes them too soft to store easily. A team led by Dr Donald Grierson of Nottingham University working with ICI Seeds have used anti-sense genes to make tomatoes that stay hard while they ripen naturally, acquiring a full, natural flavour along the way.

The softening is caused by an enzyme. Donald Grierson's team cloned the gene for the softening enzyme, and turned it back to front to make it into an anti-gene. Then this anti-gene was inserted into a cell from a tomato plant and the cell was grown into a complete new plant, with the anti-sense gene in all its cells. This anti-sense gene produced anti-sense RNA in every cell which cancelled out 90 per cent of the message from the gene for the softening enzyme. The effect was that very little of the softening enzyme was made and tests showed that the tomatoes from the plant with the extra genes stayed hard as they ripened.

Other fruit may be protected against bruising in storage in the same way. Another group at Durham University are using anti-sense RNA for a different purpose; to improve the properties of some cooking oils by cancelling out messages from unwanted genes for deleterious chemicals.

Anti-sense RNA clearly has a big future in agriculture and other areas when what is needed is a controlled reduction in the amount of some substances produced by a plant. Naturally decaffeinated coffee is another possibility. Whether this anti-sense technique will be valuable in defending humans against infections, where a 100 per cent effective cancelling out of the message, not just a reduction, is required to stop viral replication, remains to be seen. But Dr Conrad Lichtenstein of Imperial College London, who is working on anti-sense RNA as a means of protecting plants against viruses, thinks that in a year or two it may be shown to work, for plants at least.

Anti-genes can be inserted into plants, so that disease resistance for whatever property is conferred by the anti-genes is passed on to future generations. Used to protect against viruses, anti-genes could have the enormous potential advantage that they could make plants resistant to organisms against which neither they nor any other plants have any natural resistance.

One of the most advanced projects using genetic engineering to try to protect plants against disease is one which is using a natural parasite of a virus to defend against the virus. The virus is cucumber mosaic virus, which attacks not only cucumbers but also lettuces, tomatoes, peppers and other crops.

It is hard to imagine a parasite preying on anything as small and simple as a virus. After all a virus is nothing but a set of genetic instructions for making more virus. These are kept wrapped inside a simple protein coat until the virus gets inside a cell, when it takes off its coat to get down to work.

But the cucumber mosaic virus does have a parasite, a small piece of nucleic acid – genetic material called satellite RNA. This replicates along with the virus. It cannot replicate on its own and when it is present the virus replicates more slowly, causing milder symptoms in the plants it infects.

This led Dr David Baylcombe of the Cambridge Plant Breeding Institute and Dr Bryan Harrison of the Scottish Crop Research Institute in Dundee to try a technique already well known for the control of insect pests, but new to the world of viruses. This is biological pest control, in which a natural enemy of a pest is introduced to kill it. Doctors Baylcombe and Harrison went a step further. They decided to make the plants which needed to be protected against cucumber mosaic virus produce the biological control agent themselves. They made plants which are attacked by cucumber mosaic virus produce satellite RNA to parasitize the virus.

Doing this was quite complicated. First the satellite RNA was isolated and then its message was copied into the form of DNA, to allow it to take the form of a plant gene. Then the gene made in this way was inserted into *Agrobacterium*. Next the *Agrobacterium* with the added gene was used to infect individual plant cells. It duly inserted the gene for the satellite RNA, along with its own genes, into the nuclei of the plant cells.

The infected cells were persuaded to grow into complete new plants with the added gene in all their cells, including those which later produced pollen or ova. Thus the ability to produce satellite RNA was passed on to future generations. Finally, the plants were infected with cucumber mosaic virus. The plants showed no symptoms of disease. Clearly the satellite RNA produced by the inserted gene is as effective in parasitizing the virus and reducing its ability to cause damage as is satellite RNA carried by the virus itself.

The first plant to be protected by satellite RNA, has been, once again, the tobacco plant as its genetics are well known, it is easy to manipulate and it is not a food crop. Before satellite RNA can be used to protect food crops researchers will have to make sure that it causes no toxic effects. If, as seems likely, there are no such effects it should be possible to use satellite RNA to make varieties of lettuce, tomato, peppers, cucumbers and other crops which are resistant to cucumber mosaic virus.

It may also be possible to find satellite RNAs that prey on other viruses, and to implant genes for them into other crops so as to make them resistant to the other viruses. Those responsible will also have to be sure that they can prevent the spread of satellite RNA to other plants where it might be harmful, by removing the genetic instructions which allow such spread.

Another technique for plant protection, which is now being developed in several laboratories, resembles vaccination. In one new technique for vaccinating humans, (described earlier in the chapter about new vaccines) the gene for one antigen in the coat of a virus particle is introduced into the human body (by a harmless virus) where the viral antigen is then produced. The human immune system then forms antibodies against the antigen and the rest of the immune system becomes alerted to the virus involved and will instantly attack it if it ever infects the body.

Something remarkably similar is now being tried in plants. Plants don't have immune systems like animals. But they have their own defences against infection. Part of these is an ability, once part of a virus has got inside a plant, to attack the whole virus if it later infects the plant.

Just how the attack is carried out is unknown. But then, as plant biochemists point out in strong language, resources for their subject have generally been neglected in favour of animal and human biochemistry, to the point where plant biochemistry is several years behind even in understanding such basically important things as resistance to disease. But plant genetic engineering has run so far ahead that it's proving possible to test the idea of vaccinating plants without understanding how it works, and even to try out ideas in plants which may later be useful in animals and humans too.

Dr Roger Beachy of the Monsanto company in St Louis has already inserted genes for a protein from a virus, the tobacco mosaic virus, into tobacco plants and shown that the plants are made resistant to infection with the virus. In the last two years, five separate 'vaccines' to protect plants against virus diseases, using virus coat protein genes inserted into the plants, have been developed and demonstrated. Tomato plants have been vaccinated against tomato mosaic virus and found to be completely protected against the virus. If the genes are inserted into reproductive cells, then not only the plants but their descendants are protected for ever.

Now, with the new financial support engendered by the commercial promise of plant biotechnology, plant biochemists are working to understand how plant immunity works. In this they are still several years behind immunologists studying human immunology. But in terms of applying their findings, because there are no ethical problems in research on plants, the plant genetic engineers have jumped ahead and are now showing human gene therapists the way ahead.

It is almost certainly already possible to provide humans and their descendants with perpetual immunity to virus and other diseases in the same way as the plant engineers have done it. That is, by inserting a gene for an antigenic, immunity-stimulating coat protein from a virus into the human genome of a human egg cell. The human who grew from such an egg – and his or her descendants – would make the viral protein in all their cells and the immune system would react against it by making antibodies and becoming alerted to the virus. It might also be possible to protect people against some viruses by making their own and their descendants' bodies produce satellite RNAs, since satellite RNAs probably parasitize some human as well as plant viruses. Even if they don't it should not be beyond the wit of genetic engineers to invent parasites for human viruses.

It will probably be a long time before anyone will venture to insert such genes into human eggs. At present medical opinion is overwhelmingly against adding genes of any kind to human eggs, no matter how beneficial, because of fears of unpredictable harmful side effects either in the person who grows from the egg or in his or her descendants. But in the long term, alluring techniques shown to work in the easier-to-experiment-in field of plant and, later, animal genetics will be forcing themselves into the consciousness of the more cautious human genetic engineers. Already plant geneticists are donating actual genetic components for use in human and animal biotechnology.

In the course of many millions of years of evolution, plant viruses have become extraordinarily efficient at their way of life, at entering and taking over control of plant cells and then replicating themselves inside the cells. These functions are carried out by highly specialized sets of genetic instructions – sequences of viral DNA. These specialized sets of instructions can be easily, as it were, unscrewed from a virus's genes and screwed into quite different genes, where the instructions will have just the same effect as they did in the virus, because the language of DNA is universal.

I said in the introduction to this book that we are making our genes, which used to be our slavemasters, into our servants. It is also true that we are making those old and bitter enemies, the viruses, into powerful allies. Both human viruses and plant viruses are now being dismantled and the genetic instructions which have enabled them to starve, cripple and kill us, are increasingly being put to work for the benefit of humankind. In a few years, perhaps by the turn of the century, the benefits obtained from viruses dismantled and redeployed may outweigh the harm they cause, so potent for good as well as evil are the powers they contain.

One leading researcher in this field, Dr Michael Wilson of the John Innes Institute near Norwich calls plant viruses a 'Toolbox' for genetic engineering and crop protection. One tool which Wilson and others have already fished out of the box, and begun to use is a tool for cutting up genes. New viral genes are produced as endless strings of repeated sequences, rather like toilet rolls needing to be torn into separate sheets at the perforations. The sequence that does this can be programmed to do the same thing to other sequences of genetic material.

One idea now being worked on is to insert the 'gene scissors', as they have been nicknamed, into crop plants, having first re-programmed the scissors, by adding new sets of instructions to them, to chop up and mutilate any viral genes which get into the plant's cells. The scissors would sit harmlessly in the cell until a virus appeared and began to replicate by making its messenger RNA. At that point, the scissors (which are RNA not DNA choppers) would be activated and would chop the messenger up into meaningless little bits. The message to make virus would never get through to the ribosomes. No more virus would be made.

When plant viruses infect cells, they are remorselessly efficient in subverting the cells to their needs. The gene transcribing machinery of all an infected plant's cells is diverted from its normal task of making the many thousands of proteins the plant needs for healthy life, and subverted to making endless copies of the virus.

Much remains to be learnt about how viruses do this. But one of the main bits of virus involved has been identified. This is a sequence tacked onto one end of messenger RNAs sent into infected cells by the tobacco mosaic virus. Doubtless other viruses have similar sequences. This one, in the words of Michael Wilson, 'Avidly recruits host cell factors and the ribosomes involved in protein synthesis to the cause of making virus protein.'

The tables have now been turned however, and this supremely subversive agent has now been recruited to protect crops (not only tobacco), which suffer from the effects of cell-enslaving viruses. Dr Wilson uncoupled the subversing sequence from the tobacco virus and coupled it onto other genes, which he then inserted in the usual way into plant, animal and bacterial cell cultures. Whatever gene the subversive sequence was attached to, or whatever cell culture it was inserted into, the expression of the gene was enhanced. In other words the added sequence always subverted the cells to direct more effort to making the gene's product, just as it subverts cells infected with tobacco mosaic virus to make more virus.

What genetic engineers have here is a message they can tack onto the gene for anything they want to make in any cell, which holds a gun to the cell's head and says 'Make more of me.' This could make the manufacture of most of the products of genetic engineering described in this book more productive, cheaper and more competitive. Says Michael Wilson 'This sequence is now being tested in about thirty laboratories worldwide, in many different projects where increased gene expression is required. We await the results with eager anticipation.' Yes indeed. Other such natural accelerators have been found and taken from viruses. That from the tobacco mosaic virus is the most effective so far, but doubtless more and even better ones will be discovered.

Another tool from the plant virus toolbox is, to mix metaphors, a set of packaging instructions. As part of its take-over of plant cells, a virus instructs the captured cell not only to make the protein coat of the virus particle, but also to wrap the virus's genetic code up in it, making neat symmetrical virus particles. The sequence for the wrapping instructions can be separated from the rest of the virus's genetics and attached to other genes. They will then be wrapped up in just the same way, creating particles so like virus particles that they have been christened 'Pseudovirus' particles.

Michael Wilson's group have done this and produced pseudovirus particles with, for example, a small piece of poliovirus DNA packaged inside a protein coat. Such packages could be used as vaccines. Because such a pseudovirus particle resembles a real virus particle in its structure and shape – having been made to the same instructions – it should be good at stimulating immunity, unlike some vaccines made by genetic engineering which don't look enough like the real thing to stimulate immunity properly.

The packaging instructions are highly efficient. Like other genetic instructions they also contain means of enforcing the instructions which, for plant viruses, are especially forceful. So vaccines made in this way, by tagging plant virus packaging instructions onto human virus coat proteins, could be made very productively and so perhaps very cheaply.

There are more tools lying around in the plant virus toolbox ready to be picked up, and no doubt others waiting in animal and human virus toolboxes as well. Even those few described here have a formidable range of potential uses; making new vaccines more efficiently than today's; making new medical drugs; protecting plants – and perhaps one day animals and even humans – against infections by using gene scissors.

In describing the plant virus toolbox I have glossed over an extra bit of gene shifting involved in it which for the sake of completeness ought to be described. It once again demonstrates the advanced state of the art today. Out of 632 known plant viruses the majority, 484, are made not of DNA but of RNA. RNA you will remember is the form into which genes made of DNA in plant cell nuclei are copied to send as messengers to the ribosomes, where their messages are translated into new proteins. So RNA viruses do not have to be copied into messengers, they *are* messengers. But in order for their tool kits to be plundered for the use of human genetic engineers, the sequences which are the wanted tools have to be copied into the form of DNA.

This is now easily and routinely done using an enzyme, Reverse Transcriptase. Once a bit of plant virus RNA, a tool out of the tool kit, has been copied into DNA it can be treated like a gene and attached to other bits of DNA to implant in cells. The packaging instructions, the make-it-faster instructions, and the genetic scissors described above are translated into DNA by reverse transcriptase before being tacked on to other genes. Then, when these instructions are needed, their sequences are copied to RNA, making messengers to send to ribosomes. And up pop the tools from the tool kits in their original form of RNA. Very clever.

The first genetically-engineered plant to be grown on a large scale in the UK will almost certainly be the potato. Back in 1987, two new genes were inserted into a well-known variety of potato, the pink Desiree. Shoots growing from cells with the added genes (added, by the way, using good old *Agrobacterium*) grew into potato plants which were found to express the added genes. Having shown the technique works using useless and harmless marker genes, the team responsible at the Cambridge Plant Breeding Institute are now working to insert useful genes into Desiree.

Only some of the possible uses for genetic engineering in plant breeding have been described here. Besides resistance to insects and viruses, there are genes for resistance to heat or cold to be built in to allow crops to be grown over new areas of the Earth's surface. They will help nations to meet the challenge of the Greenhouse Effect, expected to cause changes in climate with what are now temperate belts of the USA and USSR becoming semi-tropical.

If the genes responsible for the production of cyanide could be deleted from two very important tropical crops, cassava and taro, and genes for higher protein content inserted into them, then diet and consequently health over huge areas of Africa especially could be greatly improved, at relatively low cost. This now looks possible.

Crops able to grow in salty or waterlogged soils may soon be produced by adding in the necessary genes from other plants that have naturally colonized such soils, but don't interfere with the crops. Huge tracts of new land for agriculture could be colonized.

The major consequences of genetic engineering in plant breeding will include a shift towards inbuilt protection against pests by the plants' own genes and away from the use of chemicals; herbicides and pesticides. But legislation and a firm hand will be needed to provide the right incentives and controls for big companies who make much of their living from agrochemicals to move in these directions.

The growing use of genetic engineering should also bring a new appreciation of the value of the diversity of the planetary gene bank. We know quite a lot today about how to shift existing, beneficial genes from one organism to another. We know almost nothing about how to create beneficial genes. We will only learn how to create new such genes by studying many existing ones. Every species deleted from the planetary gene bank by its extinction stunts the future growth of biotechnology that bit more. Genes are a renewable resource, but only if we let them be.

14

FLORA OR FRANKENSTEIN: RELEASE INTO THE ENVIRONMENT

The first few genetically engineered plants and bacteria are now beginning to move out of the lab and go to work in the fields. Such 'Releases into the Environment' as they are dramatically called, have been the subject of great concern. What is being released and how much real cause for concern is there?

When gene cloning in laboratory bacterial cultures began, there was much talk of the possible escape from the lab. of bacteria which could be made abnormally virulent by their extra genes. In fact it proved easy to prevent any such escape by building dependence on laboratory food supplies into the bacteria. It also proved to be the case that bacteria and other organisms with genes added for cloning purposes by genetic engineers are weaker than natural bacteria and have little or no chance of surviving, let alone flourishing, in the wild.

Genes added for the selfish purposes of genetic engineers represent no advantage, but in fact substantial disadvantages, to the bacteria on whom they are inflicted. *E. coli* engineered to manufacture insulin, or thermophiles endowed with a great capacity for catalysing the transformation of one kind of fat into another, for example, don't gain any benefit from these talents – useful as they are to the pharmaceutical or food industries.

Fear of accidental release proved groundless. But now plants as well as bacteria with added genes are beginning to be deliberately released. Let's look at examples. Best known are the so-called 'Ice-minus' bacteria. Crops are often damaged by frost because their own natural resistance to freezing is countered by bacteria living on the plants, which encourage the formation of ice crystals and so trigger the freezing process, which damages leaves and helps the bacteria infect the plants. By introducing a competitive strain of the same bacterium, *pseudomonas syringae*, which has been genetically engineered so it no longer causes ice nuclei to form, Californian scientists have shown they can reduce frost damage to crops. Advanced Genetic Science of Oakwood, California, hope to market Ice-minus strains of *P. syringae* and other bacteria, in the 1990s under the name 'Frostban'.

In the UK a team at the Oxford Institute of Virology have prepared and tested baculoviruses which infect caterpillars (described fully in 'The Pharmaceutical Farmyard') as a pest control agent for the Pine Beauty Moth, which causes heavy damage to the pine forests in Scotland. The virus used has been genetically crippled by deleting the gene for its protein coat. This leaves the virus still able to infect and kill the caterpillars of the moth but no longer able to survive outside caterpillars without the tough protein coat to protect each virus particle. This means the engineered virus is unable to spread and interbreed with other baculoviruses to create new and dangerous species. Also in the UK virus-resistant potatoes created by genetic engineering have been field-tested.

A Monsanto team have taken the gene for a natural pesticide from one bacterium, *Bacillus thuringiensis*, and transferred it to *Pseudomonas fluorescens*, a harmless bacterium, that lives around plant roots. This has been tested in the lab and shown to be effective in protecting plants against soil pests. Monsanto's and other researchers have also added *B. thuringiensis* genes to tobacco plants and shown this protects them from pest attack in the field.

Away from the area of plant protection, bacteria able to feed on pollutants such as PCBs are being developed, (as described in 'Greening Industry') and are soon to undergo field trials, in attempts to clean up accumulations of these toxic chemicals. In medicine, live vaccinia virus, the virus used to vaccinate to protect against smallpox until that disease was eliminated, is now being used to carry genes from several other disease organisms, hopefully to protect against all of them when used as a vaccine.

That is not a complete list of all the genetically-altered organisms which have been, or are about to be, released from the lab into the outer world. But it is typical of the purposes for which bacteria or plants, in the main, are having genes added to them for. What dangers, if any, do such experiments represent? Let's look at the various possibilities in turn.

A question continually asked is whether introducing genes by artificial means rather than by normal reproduction, which is not only different in kind but also allows an almost infinitely wider range of new genes to be introduced into an organism, could itself lead to the creation of organisms with unexpected new and harmful properties.

Many thousands of such gene transfers have now been carried out. The results have invariably shown that the organisms with the new genes have only the predicted properties. They behave like the parent organisms except for new traits conferred as expected by the new gene. Any unexpected change is minor and disadvantageous, making the organisms less likely to survive. There was never any reason to suppose that genes might have unexpected effects because they came from unrelated organisms. Experience confirms that they have no such effects.

A second question often raised is whether plants or bacteria – or even in the future animals – with added genes may behave like non-native species introduced into new environments, like the rabbit into Australia for example, or the *Legionella* bacteria which are harmless in springs but proliferate in air conditioning systems, or the predatory fish which escaped from a farm in Panama and exterminated most other species in a nearby lake, or the gypsy moth, or the starling, which have caused devastation in new environments.

The answer is that these creatures or organisms cause devastation in a new environment because they differ significantly, in complex ways, from other organisms already in the same environment. Genetically-engineered bacteria or plants, on the other hand, do not differ at all from their close relatives in the environment in their general behaviour. They differ only in some specialized property.

While problems could be caused by introducing a genetically-engineered bacterium, for example to a new environment, the problems would be caused by the original properties of the bacterium, not by those donated by its extra gene. In other words, it is necessary to control the release of organisms with added genes into new environments no more and no less carefully than the release of any other organisms. In fact, most uses for genetically-engineered micro-organisms involve releasing them into the same environment that they originally came from. So the problem will seldom arise.

Another question asked is whether introducing new genes could accidentally convert a crop plant into a new weed, or a harmless bacterium into a new pathogen (disease-causing organism). The answer is, that weeds and pathogens have become adapted to their roles by many millions of years of evolution. Their respective abilities to survive and grow without human encouragement and in the face of every discouragement, and to cause diseases in the course of reproducing, depend on the highly-evolved co-operation of large numbers of their genes. Introducing one or two other genes for quite other purposes has only the effect those genes have naturally. It won't make weeds tougher or bacteria more infectious. Adding a few genes with known effects never causes new and wholly unexpected properties to appear.

There is however a real danger that a valuable property incorporated into a crop plant could spread by outbreeding into a weed species, unless stringent precautions are taken. If genes for herbicide resistance are taken from soil bacteria, where they exist naturally, and incorporated permanently into the germ lines of many crops, then it may not be long before pollen from such a transgenic crop chances to fertilize a wild variety of the same plant on the edge of a field. Unless the transgenic weed were spotted and eliminated very fast, it would soon spread beyond control. Genetic engineers would inadvertently have created a real menace, a weed that would need ten times as much herbicide to kill it as any weed today.

So much for genetic engineers' promises to reduce mankind's dependence on chemicals. This must be prevented by ensuring that herbicide-resistance genes are transferred only into crops that cannot pollinate other plants.

Summing up, it is clear that putting one or two extra genes into plants or bacteria for clearly defined purposes, to make the bacteria produce valuable pharmaceutical products or pesticides to protect crop plants, or to make plants more productive or less liable to damage, is not going to create new weeds or disease organisms. It takes millions of years to evolve the efficiency of a weed or a pathogen – as genetic engineers who are now busy taking advantage of the various genes involved well know.

There are real potential hazards. A genetically-altered bacterium released in a part of the world where it doesn't occur naturally could upset local ecology and have unexpected effects. A crop plant endowed with high resistance to herbicides could spread that resistance to weeds of the same species, by fertilizing them with its pollen. But these hazards are quite easily avoidable, by techniques as simple as those used to prevent other hazards in plant breeding and pest control which involve no genetic engineering. The hazards are small compared to the enormous benefits genetic engineering can bring in reducing dependence on herbicides and–pesticides, raising productivity, resisting drought and enabling new arid or salty ground to be cultivated.

What about biological *weapons*? Will genetic engineering find applications there? As yet genetic engineers can only imitate the deadly efficiency with which billions of years of evolution has polished the performance of viruses and bacteria, they cannot improve on it. But it is certainly now possible to create new artificial strains of infective organisms, by altering the genes for coat proteins, so that a virus for example is no longer recognized as foreign by the immune system of some one infected by it. In this way new epidemics could be caused.

It must be emphasized that this will not be done accidentally in the course of other experiments. Inserting genes for known functions will not create new strains against which the immune system will have no resistance. But it could be done deliberately. It would however require much more advanced equipment than the making of nerve gases, which can be made as easily as insecticides. It would require very advanced containment, otherwise the maker would suffer worse than the intended victim.

Biological weapons would be slow-acting, would require advanced scientific skills and equipment, would be liable to affect civil as well as military personnel and liable to infect the invader as well as those under attack unless the whole population were vaccinated. It is hard to see what advantages over various combinations of nuclear, conventional and chemical weapons biological weapons, genetically-engineered or otherwise, could really have.

149

15

THE PHARMACEUTICAL FARMYARD

In the last five years it has become possible to insert genes into animals. Not only into their body cells so the genes are expressed and their products made during the life of a single animal, but also into their germ cells, the cells which produce sperms or eggs. Not only the animal into the germ cells of which the genes are inserted but also its descendants carry the extra genes and produce the gene's products.

The creation of such 'Transgenic' animals, as they have been christened, is an important development for two reasons. It holds out great promise for agriculture and will allow it to take completely new directions. It is also true that what can be done with animals could, undoubtedly, be done for humans.

The obvious uses for genetic engineering in farm animals are in improving their desirable qualities; increasing milk production, producing faster-growing, leaner carcasses, building in disease resistance. This kind of improvement can be attempted by genetic engineering in two ways. Either by cloning a control substance, growth hormone, for example in the laboratory and injecting it into animals to supplement their own production. Or by inserting the gene for growth hormone into the animal itself, preferably into its germ cells so that the gene and the consequent ability to make the required hormone is inherited by all the animals' progeny. Both approaches are now being tried, with both successes and problems emerging.

Less obvious and perhaps more exciting is the new ability brought about by genetic engineering to create the 'Pharmaceutical Farmyard', in which farm animals will be used as living bioreactors to produce high-value substances. In the main these will be human body control substances, such as insulin or blood clotting factors, made by inserting the appropriate cloned human genes into farm animals together with control sequences which will make the human genes produce their products only in the appropriate part of the animal. Human genes will be 'switched on' in the udder of a cow for example, so that the wanted human product can then be simply extracted from milk. It has already been done, though not yet in cows. Sheep are producing blood clotting Factor IX, a substance missing in some haemophiliacs due to a genetic defect.

A problem (also mentioned in the chapter 'Gene Therapy') has emerged in this work, the problem of getting the gene to the right place. While living cells have generally proved to be remarkably, even surprisingly tolerant of extra genes crudely thrust into them by genetic engineers, it is also clear that in order for genes to work most efficiently, and in order for them to be passed on reliably to further generations, it is often necessary to place the genes very precisely at exactly the right sites in the chromosomes – the microscopic rods of DNA in which genes are arranged in the nuclei of living cells.

This need to target genes to the right places in chromosomes will become more important in the next generation of genetic engineering, when not just single genes but groups of genes will be transplanted from one organism to another. Many useful or advantageous characteristics, such as the ability of plants to fix nitrogen from the air, are conferred by the products not of one but of several genes. The relative positions of the various members of such a group of genes on chromosomes is sometimes important, even crucially so to their proper working.

In the last year or two scientists have developed and demonstrated techniques for directing implanted genes to precise sites in the chromosomes they are to inhabit. This gene targeting, first achieved in mice, but doubtless also possible for plants – and, if permitted, for humans too – represents a massive leap forward in genetic engineering. It's described in more detail later.

The potential ability of hormones, the body's natural chemical messengers, to increase food value or milk production in animals has been known for many years. But the prohibitive cost of extracting hormones from animals, and the impossibility of synthesizing their large protein molecules artificially, prevented hormones being used on a large scale until the advent of genetic engineering. The ability to shift the gene for a hormone out of an animal and into laboratory cell cultures so as to clone it has made hormones readily available.

In 1985 Monsanto scientists succeeded in producing cloned bovine somatotrophin, BST, a hormone normally produced naturally in a cow's pituitary gland, which stimulates the cow to convert feed into more milk rather than into body fat. In 1988 cloned BST was injected into thousands of dairy cows. Milk yields were increased by up to 25 per cent with no significant ill effects on the health of the animals and no effects at all on the chemical composition of the milk.

Pig somatotrophin, (PST) produced in a similar fashion, given to pigs in the last six to eight weeks before they are marketed, increases the animals' growth rate and produces leaner pork. BST made by cow and PST made by pig genes are species specific; they have no effects in humans and so are safe for humans to consume even if animal carcasses containing them contain minutely more than the usual traces of hormones as a result of injections. The need for frequent injections of such hormones into animals can be eliminated by using implanted pellets which release the hormone gently at a controlled rate.

BST and PST implants have the potential not only to allow cattle and pigs to achieve milk yields and meat quality equivalent to or better than that of the best pedigree herds, leapfrogging twenty years of selective breeding in the process, but also to allow farmers to adjust meat or milk production precisely to meet varying demand.

But in spite of the potential of hormone injections for lowering costs and prices without harming animals or consumers, the reactions of both farmers and the public to the use of BST have so far been unenthusiastic. There are fears about human health and animal welfare – both almost completely unjustified. There is also concern about upsets in economics the technique could cause as farmers able to apply it become much more competitive than others.

One objection to the use of BST is the need to administer it by daily injection. While using implanted slow-release pellets could go some way to overcome this objection, it would still lead to unnatural concentrations of hormone around the site of release. Some people fear this could cause side effects in consumers. An ingenious alternative is being developed at the Hannah Research Institute in the UK, which could lead to growth and other hormones having to be injected only once in an animal's life.

The technique goes like this. First the hormone involved, BST for example, is injected into the bodies of mice, which make anti-bodies against it because BST is a foreign substance to the mice. These antibodies are then made as monoclonal antibodies in the usual way, and then they are injected into cattle. The cattle make antibodies to the antibodies: anti-antibodies. Antibodies fit around the molecules they react with like a glove around a hand. The antibody to BST fits around the BST molecule like a glove around the hand of the BST molecule. The antibody to the antibody to BST must therefore be like the original hand inside the glove, in other words it will mimic the structure of BST.

So, by injecting antibody to BST into cattle, the cattle are made to make more of a substance which mimics BST so closely that, with a bit of luck, it will behave like BST. Since antibody produc-tion continues long after the injection of the substance against which antibodies are formed, the effect of the injected antibody is to make the cattle go on making the BST-like substance for a long time.

So here is a way to make cattle make higher levels of what is effectively BST for long periods, by a single injection. So far the scientists responsible have shown that the 'anti-antibodies' mimic-king BST do stimulate cell receptors in the same way as BST itself, and that they do stimulate animals to put on weight faster. It remains to be seen how long the effects will last and just what an impact they will make.

If it works, the same technique could be used more widely. Injections of antibodies against other hormones which farm live-stock need in larger quantities might be given with other injections to young animals as a matter of routine.

A further advantage could be that only the particular, wanted effect of a hormone could be selected from among many effects by using the anti-antibody technique. BST, for example, has a large, complex molecule which has several different potent effects. It not only promotes the formation of muscle tissue but also raises blood sugar and breaks down fat.

Just a small part of the BST molecule with one particular effect could be isolated, and only that part of the BST molecule would be made. Cattle injected with the antibody to it could then be induced to make not complete BST but only the part of the BST molecule with the desired effect, high milk yield for example, as an anti-antibody. In this way farm animals could be modified in very well-controlled ways.

Another, more direct way to increase the production of a hormone in an animal is to implant extra genes for the hormone into the animal itself. As long ago as 1982, a long time in genetic engineering, Dr David Palmiter became famous when he produced the giant mouse that graces the cover of this book. He injected a gene for a human growth hormone, attached to a control sequence to promote expression of the gene, into the nuclei of fertilized mouse eggs. One in three mice which grew from the eggs had the human gene incorporated into their genomes. Some of the offspring of the mice had the added gene too.

Since then scientists have refined the techniques for inserting genes into animal egg cells, improved the success rate in mice and begun to insert genes into larger and more useful animals. In the last two years human growth hormone genes have been inserted into pig and sheep cells. But the technique is still some way from application. Although pigs with added growth hormone genes had dramatically reduced levels of fat and metabolized their feed more efficiently, they tend to suffer from arthritis and to be infertile. And only one in two hundred of the eggs injected with growth genes actually grew into animals in which the wanted genes worked.

But results are likely to improve. Those to date have been obtained by implanting genes for human or cattle growth hormone into sheep or pigs, because these were the only growth hormones available. These hormones are quite species specific, so it is not surprising that their effects have been limited. Pig growth hormone is now becoming available. The first results of the effects of extra genes for this hormone implanted into pigs, very recently reported, suggest that it may produce bigger and leaner pigs without adverse side-effects.

There is some way to go before genes can be routinely

implanted into animals to create new breeds of improved food-producers. The ability to target genes to exactly where they are required in the genome, already mentioned, should help things along. More of that later. First we should look at progress with a more radical idea, that of converting farm animals into living bioreactors. As Dr John Clark of the Institute of Animal Physiology and Genetics Research in Edinburgh, a world leader in the field puts it, the idea is to, 'engineer the cell on the hoof.'

John Clark and his colleagues have already produced sheep which secrete two valuable human control substances in their milk. The substances are; Factor IX, which is one of the substances required for the proper clotting of blood, and antitrypsin, which is wanted to treat some lung diseases. The transgenic sheep – living bioreactors – were created by injecting cloned human genes for antitrypsin and Factor IX into sheep egg cells and reimplanting the egg cells into the mothers' wombs to develop and be born normally.

So as to make the sheeps' bodies produce the wanted substances only in the udder and so into their milk, Dr Clark added control sequences to the genes, which ensure that they are only switched on in the milk-producing tissue of the udder. Both Factor IX and antitrypsin were indeed produced into the sheeps' milk, and the genes for them have been passed on to some of the sheeps' progeny.

So far the quantities of antitrypsin and Factor IX produced by these transgenic sheep are too low to make the process commercially attractive. But now that the idea has been shown to work, a lot of research is going on to find ways of improving its efficiency. The low success rate to date in getting genes into sheeps' eggs and making them work there is partly due to the very crude genetic engineering technique used. This involves simply injecting solutions of genes into fertilized eggs with hypodermics. Better techniques now being developed and tested include the use of viruses which naturally insert their genes among animal genes, so-called retroviruses, also being developed for human gene therapy. By delivering the added genes right in among the animal's own genes, retroviruses could raise the success rate of gene implants ten to a hundredfold.

Transgenic animals have much to offer as living bioreactors. Unlike the cultures of bacteria such as *E. coli* now mainly used, animals make human products in exactly the same form as do human cells, because the cells of cows and sheep work in the same way as ours. And unlike any cell cultures, once a breed of cow or sheep permanently making a valuable pharmaceutical product has been established, it doesn't need a lab to live in.

Transgenic cows making, for example, blood clotting factor, antitrypsin and insulin – there is no reason why multiple genes should not be inserted into the same transgenic animal – would live and feed just like any other cows, but they would make a lot more money for their owners. From the humane point of view, they would doubtless also be treated better because of the investment they represented.

To those who believe that any animal farming is exploitation, then a pharmaceutical farmyard is no better or worse than any other. To those who accept farming in principle but are concerned at cruelty and unnatural environments, transgenic animals need not be a cause for concern, given proper regulation. Extra genes need have no unpleasant side effects on animals. Nonetheless, proper controls will be needed to ensure that animals are not cruelly eploited by being kept in increasingly artificial conditions to facilitate extraction of high value products. It will also be necessary to ensure that extra genes don't cause suffering by leading to painful or behaviour-distorting abnormalities.

Perhaps a little further in the future than the pharmaceutical farmyard is the grazing pig. Ruminants are able to live by grazing because in their complicated stomachs are colonies of bacteria which can break down cellulose, the tough material of which plant cell walls are made, to simpler sugars which the cow or sheep can digest. One obvious target for genetic engineers is to insert more genes for the enzymes that break down cellulose – cellulases – into ruminant gut bacteria and reimplant the bacteria into cows and sheep to digest more food.

It may also be possible to insert genes into gut bacteria for enzymes that break down lignin, the hard substance of which dry wood is made. Some fungi have such enzymes and the genes for them could in principle be transferred to bacteria.

Another possibility is to insert genes for cellulases into bacteria which live in silage, the pickled grass used as a winter feed for cattle. It is hoped the bacteria would break down the cell walls of the grass to digestible sugars, and so increase the food value of silage.

With such targets in mind, several teams of scientists are

working to clone genes for cellulases. Prominent among them are Doctors Harry Gilbert and Judith Hall of Newcastle University's Department of Agricultural and Environmental Science. They have identified over twenty cellulases made by bacteria and cloned some of their genes, and are excited by the recent demonstration that genes from bacteria will work in higher animals. The reverse, making animals genes work in bacteria, is of course the basis of most gene cloning. But until recently no one had seen much point in moving bacteria genes into animals.

Gilbert and Hall are hoping to create a transgenic pig able to live by grazing because it could digest cellulose, not like cows and sheep by courtesy of bacteria in its gut but by its own, transgenic abilities. Pigs lack the elaborate stomachs of cows and sheep and the bacteria which digest cellulose in them would not survive in pigs. But an alternative may be to insert genes for a specially efficient cellulase, taken from bacteria, into the egg cell of a pig, with the gene targetted to a site next to the gene for the pig's own digestive enzyme, trypsin.

Trypsin is produced by the pancreas of the pig and poured into the gut down a duct. Hall and Gilbert believe that genetic engineering could ensure that the pig with the cellulase gene made cellulase after a meal so as to digest cellulose in the pig's food, just as it made trypsin. Pig food could then incorporate a lot more plant material relative to other constituents than it does today.

Transgenic chickens as well as cattle are being created. Dr Robert Bosselman of the Californian genetic engineering company, Amgen, has produced the world's first healthy chickens containing genes from other animals. Not only the chickens themselves but some of their offspring carried the extra genes. In a few years transgenic chickens could be laying eggs worth more than their weight in gold.

This isn't the first time that genes have been inserted into chickens. But in the earlier experiments harmful viruses had to be used to insert the genes, and they made the chickens seriously ill. Such viruses couldn't be used to produce proper transgenic chickens, it would be both inhumane and uneconomic. The technique used by Dr Bosselman does the chickens no harm and Amgen are already planning to use it commercially in potentially profitable ways.

Dr Bosselman does use a virus to insert the genes into the

chickens, but it is a virus that has been genetically engineered to make it harmless. Viruses of the type called retroviruses are ideal for use in this way because they naturally insert their own genes right in among the genes of the cells they infect.

The gene that the scientists want to insert into the chicken is first inserted into the virus, using standard genetic engineering techniques. Then the virus is allowed to infect a chick embryo, by injecting it through the shell of an egg into the embryo inside. The virus infects most of the cells of the embryo. Once it has entered a cell the virus does not replicate any further because it has been engineered not to, so it causes no harm to the growing embryo.

When the chicken pecks its way out of the egg and grows into a hen or a cockerel, it carries the added gene in most of its cells including, in some chickens at least, the reproductive cells. So here is a system for inserting new genes into chickens and their descendants for ever.

Amgen see transgenic chickens being made for three purposes. First to provide the chickens with natural immunity to the fatal virus diseases that proliferate so easily in broiler houses. Earlier experiments have shown that if a gene for part of the coat of a virus is inserted into a chicken then the viral coat protein is made inside the chicken. It blocks all the receptors on the surfaces of cells that live virus could have otherwise entered by. This makes the chicken invulnerable to the virus. Amgen think this technique will be ready for use in one or two years.

A second use for implanted genes will be to make chickens grow faster. This has already been done with other animals such as mice and pigs, but, says Dr Bosselman, scientists don't yet know enough about how the growth of chickens is controlled to do the same thing for them. So superchicks are perhaps four or five years away.

The third idea is the most sensational. It is to use chickens as living bioreactors to produce high value medical drugs neatly packaged in eggs. Among the drugs of the future, already coming into use today, are the human body's natural control substances; interferon, insulin and so on. While an egg is growing inside a hen's body, the protein albumen, the main constituent of egg white, is made inside the egg at a very high rate. A chicken's egg makes one gram of albumen a day as it grows, inside and outside the body.

Amgen's plan is to remove the gene for albumen and to replace it with the gene for a valuable substance such as insulin. Then, hopefully, the chicken with the extra gene will lay eggs containing, by pharmaceutical standards, huge amounts of insulin. Even if the added gene were only to be expressed one tenth as well as the albumen gene, then ten chickens could produce one gram of insulin every day in the daily eggs they lay. Pharmaceutical poultry breeding could become very profitable indeed.

There has been concern that chickens might be genetically altered to produce wingless or featherless breeds. When I put the question to Dr Bosselman he said that Amgen were not considering research along such lines. Leaving humane considerations out of it, he pointed out that the research into the control of development needed would be immensely expensive and belong to another generation of genetic engineering, and that in any case the public would be revolted by the idea of eating such monsters.

In order to learn more about the effects of introducing new genes into animals it is necessary to discover as much as possible about how the genes involved develop right from the start.

It is very difficult to watch development going on in a mammal because it is internal and invisible. But Dr Margaret Perry of Edinburgh University has made it possible in chickens – by growing chickens on the half shell. In nature a hen's egg cells are fertilized by a cockerel's sperm in the upper part of the oviduct, the tube carrying eggs down from the ovary where they are produced. The fertilized egg starts to divide and grow as it moves down the duct. By the time the egg shell starts to form around it, twenty-four hours after fertilization, the egg has already divided many times to form an embryo with 60,000 cells in it. Twenty three days later the egg is laid and the chicken pecks its way out.

Margaret Perry's chickens develop outside the hen and out of the shell. First an egg which has just been fertilized is removed from the hen and is placed in a glass jar, on a nutrient medium. Twenty four hours later, at the stage when the shell would begin to form inside the hen, an empty egg shell with the top removed, looking like the remains of someone's breakfast, is filled with a second culture medium and the egg, by now a very early embryo, is placed inside it. Four days later, the embryo is transferred into a second topless egg shell to complete its development.

This is the first time a warm-blooded creature has completed its development from a fertilized egg wholly outside the natural surroundings. It is now possible to watch the effects of any genes added to a fertilized chicken egg all the way through development, from the first cell division to the moment when the chick pecks its way out.

Although in some ways genetic engineering has advanced startlingly fast – for example in the way in which different sequences taken from quite different sources are combined to provide a single functioning entity – in other ways it is surprisingly crude. It's analogous to surgery, in which, in spite of advanced medical technology, in the end everything depends on the body's ability to heal itself after being hacked about by the surgeon's knife.

In genetic engineering genes are blindly injected into the nuclei of cells, pushed higgledey-piggedly at random into the precisely-ordered array of the egg's own genes arranged along the chromosomes in its nuclei. The fact that injected genes not only frequently function but are sometimes even handed on to the next generation says much for the toughness, flexibility and adaptibility of the genetic code. Genes are tough. Not surprising since they were, indeed, the original survivors. 'Genetic studies with transgenic mice', says Dr Elizabeth Lacy of Oxford University's Genetics Department, 'have shown that injected genes can integrate anywhere in the mouse genome and that, once integrated, they are stably transmitted to pregnant mice. Thus it is possible to establish premanent lines of transgenic mice carrying any gene of interest.'

It is remarkable enough, if you compare the genome to any man-made machine or computer of any kind, that genes inserted blindly at random are expressed. It is even more remarkable that genes injected crudely into a fertilized egg can be handed on to every cell as an animal grows from one egg cell. It is most remarkable of all that the injected genes are sometimes expressed only in the part of the body where they should be expressed.

For example, genes for insulin which are injected into a fertilized egg cell are expressed only in the pancreas where insulin is normally made. Injected genes for making antibodies are expressed only in the white blood cells and spleen where antibodies are normally manufactured. It is clear that sometimes genes injected into egg cell nuclei at random are somehow incorporated into the whole interplay of controls within the dividing cells formed from the eggs, so that like the cell's own genes the newcomers put down at random form part of the cell's master plan.

This ability shows that the location of genes on chromosomes is sometimes unimportant. This augues well for the creation of more transgenic animals, and for those planning gene therapy for humans. It also suggests that the great ethical dilemmas which will arise when genetic engineers have the ability to use human genes to do more than cure disease may appear sooner rather than later. We should prepare for them now.

But while the siting of genes on chromosomes is unimportant for some purposes, for others it is clear that in order for genetic engineering to become a really precise tool able to reshape animals, plants and, if wanted, humans too with great reliability, it will be necessary to implant genes into chromosomes with great precision. For human genetic engineering especially, safety standards will have to be near absolute. Doctors will have to be sure that an inserted gene does not land on a site in a chromosome where not only may the gene not work itself, but where its proximity may inadvertently switch on a gene for uncontrolled growth next to the implanted gene and so cause cancer. Or the implanted gene's proximity could *switch off* a neighbouring gene whose functioning is essential to the individual's wellbeing.

Even without such drastic side effects, it is a fact that randomly injected genes in transgenic animals, while they are inherited and expressed, are seldom expressed as effectively as would ideally be required. Not nearly as much of their product is made as would be the case if they were natural genes in their proper places on chromosomes.

Fortunately genetic engineers have discovered how to direct genes to precise sites on chromosomes. Gene targetting is already here. It has even been used to correct the animal equivalent of a human disease caused by a genetic defect.

Dr Oliver Smithies and his team at Wisconsin University and David Melton and others in Edinburgh University used mice with an inherited genetic defect, which in mice as in humans causes the condition called Lesch-Nyhans syndrome which is a progress-ive and incurable brain disease.

The researchers have shown that this defect can be cured in mice. They did it by first identifying part of a gene which is missing in Lesch-Nyhans syndrome, part of the gene for the essential enzyme called HPRT. Then they synthesized the missing bit of gene and inserted it into very early mouse embryos taken from female mice carrying the defect.

The added bit of gene entered the cells of the embryo and, together with the other bits of the HPRT gene which the mouse embryo cells already possessed, provided enough cells, as the embryo's cells grew and divided, with complete HPRT genes to cure the condition. When a mouse grew from an embryo with the added bits of genes, enough of its cells had complete HPRT genes for the mouse to produce enough HPRT not to suffer from a deficiency, and so not to be affected by Lesch-Nyhans syndrome.

In order to perform this feat of mouse gene therapy, gene targetting was essential. The missing part of the HPRT gene had to be set down in a chromosome next to the part of the gene that was present, so that they would together make a complete functional gene. This was done by attaching a targetting sequence to the part of the gene that was inserted. The targetting sequence is identical to a sequence found in the DNA of the mouse immediately next to the point where the missing part of the HPRT gene ought to be. Because like DNA attracts like, this similarity attracted the inserted part of the gene to the site next to the other part of the gene which was already sitting there in the chromosome.

Very recently the same researchers have also shown that genes inserted in this way into early embryos are also handed on to the next generation. This suggests that it will be possible to prevent the occurrence of Lesch-Nyhans syndrome in humans. It will be possible – in fact it is probably already possible, since human egg cells do not differ fundamentally from mouse egg cells – to take early human embryos produced by a women carrying a defective HPRT gene, and to insert into these embryos the missing parts of the gene. This could ensure not only that the person who grew from the embryo was not affected by Lesch-Nyhans syndrome, but also that that person's descendants were similarly unaffected, because they would all inherit the complete HPRT gene.

Of course before such germ line gene therapy could be used to treat humans it would need much more thorough testing to ensure its reliability and to ensure that it had no unpredictable or undesirable side-effects, such as causing cancer by activating oncogenes, or upsetting other vital genes. But eventually this stage will be reached. The consequences are discussed in the chapter on 'Gene Therapy'.

'All in all', (said an article in *Science* magazine, 14 October 1988, reviewing progress with gene targetting) 'Researchers should soon have the ability to apply targetted gene transfer to modify whatever genes they want.' This rightly implies that there is more to gene targetting than human gene therapy. A number of other techniques besides that described here for getting genes into the right places are being developed by several research teams.

Gene targetting may be equally important in plant genetic engineering. Some of the techniques now being used to insert genes into plant cells are extremely crude, literally shot-gun-type. Blasts of tiny tungsten pellets coated with DNA fire genes into cells. Even when *Agrobacterium* or retroviruses are used as the vectors, able to carry the genes right into the nuclei and integrate them into the plant's own DNA, they are still integrated at random. Proper targetting for plants is needed to create new breeds which will breed true, with the inserted genes properly expressed for at least for as long as any genes last before natural selection or random mutation changes them in the course of natural events.

We have discussed transgenic plants and transgenic farm animals. Another creature which is going to be farmed on a vast scale as a living bioreactor is the caterpillar. Silkworm breeders have a head start in this area because they already know how to breed caterpillars on a large scale. In the next few years, enterprising silk producers are likely to diversify rapidly into pharmaceuticals, pesticides and other unexpected areas.

This comes about through the capabilities not of caterpillars themselves but of viruses that infect and kill caterpillars, known as baculoviruses. As in plant biotechnology it is the extraordinary ability of viruses to drive the cells they infect to make more virus that is being harnessed by biotechnologists. When baculoviruses infect a caterpillar they reproduce with amazing speed towards the end of its life, so much so that by the time the caterpillar dies more than half its body weight is made up of one single protein produced by the baculovirus. The protein is the one which forms the protective coat of the virus particles. It is produced in such quantities because after the death of the caterpillar the particles may have to survive for years before they enter another host caterpillar and are able to replicate again.

Clearly the virus must possess control sequences of DNA which drive the unfortunate caterpillar's cells to devote all their energies to producing the viral coat protein. If the gene for the coat protein is replaced by a gene for a valuable product then the cells of the caterpillar infected with the altered virus will be driven to make the valuable protein just as productively as they would normally make the viral coat protein. This has been demonstrated by a team led by Dr David Bishop of the Oxford Institute of Virology.

'What this actually means', says Dr Bishop, 'is that from one caterpillar one inch long, costing a penny or two to feed, we can produce three to five milligrams of a high-value substance. Anyone can produce billions of caterpillars with very cheap labour and food. So the ability to produce very, very large quantities of substances that doctors want to use in diagnostic kits, or in vaccines, or as therapeutic agents, is there.'

Products already being produced by genetically engineered baculoviruses include diagnostic kits for Hepatitis B and for HIV. Others are in the pipeline. Because of the extraordinary productivity of the baculovirus some enthusiasts believe that caterpillars are destined to become the main producers of the new superdrugs, vaccines and diagnostic reagents. Certainly they seem bound to play a very important role and are, therefore, bound to make caterpillar breeding a new agro industry. Silkworm producers are already considering how they could add on to their existing prosperity by adding pharmaceuticals to their products. Japan, China and other silk producers may get an unexpected bonus in the biotechnology business through their expertise in breeding large numbers of caterpillars in restricted spaces.

Dr Bishop, whose team are among world leaders in cloning caterpillar viruses, sees their use coming in three stages. The first, already under way, is in producing antigens, single proteins from the coats of viruses such as Hepatitis B and HIV for use in diagnostic tests for such diseases.

The second area, which will take longer to get under way because the products will be needed in much larger quantities, is the production of vaccines and human body control substances, interleukins and so on. They will be produced according to the instructions of genes taken from disease organisms or human cells.

The third area is one which particularly excites the Oxford virology team. It is much more ambitious. The idea is to use the baculoviruses to insert not just one but several foreign genes into the cells of caterpillars. There are, for example, antibiotics which are normally produced by moulds or *streptomycetes* but which are notoriously difficult to extract and process from the organisms which normally make them. The genes introduced for this sort of purpose would not be genes for products, but genes for all the enzymes needed to make products such as antibiotics. Genetically-engineered baculoviruses could be used to insert all the enzymes needed into caterpillars, which would then make the antibiotics.

There is a fourth way in which baculoviruses are being exploited and that is by increasing their natural ability to kill the insects, such as caterpillars they infect. This makes viruses into more effective pest control agents. Baculoviruses are already available as insecticides. But while they are valuable they have limitations; they tend to act too slowly while pests continue to damage the crop. Scientists of the Oxford Institute of Virology have already shown that a baculovirus from which they have removed a gene coding for part of the coat, leaving the virus semi-naked, is just as effective and specific in killing its host, but does not persist in the environment. This eliminates the dangerous possibility that the virus might mutate or recombine with other viruses to attack beneficial insects.

There is also the possibility of making baculoviruses more deadly by adding genes for deadly toxins to them, so that the viruses would kill host insects as soon as they entered them, rather than delaying till the virus had built up its numbers to killing levels. Genes for such toxins are being introduced into baculoviruses at Oxford.

Genetic engineering is being used to produce new drugs and vaccines for farm animals as well as humans. While cost considerations are more limiting in agriculture, standards for avoiding side-effects are lower than for humans, which enables more rapid progress to be made. Using genetic engineering vaccines can be made to protect against diseases caused by animal parasites which cannot be made by conventional means, because the parasites involved cannot be grown outside the animal's body. An exciting development in this area is the use of vaccinia, cowpox virus, as a carrier enabling animals to be vaccinated against several diseases simultaneously. The technique is the same as that used for humans, described earlier.

Scientists at the British Poultry Research Station at Houghton are developing vaccines made of vaccinia with genes from several other disease organisms added, to protect chicken against infectious bronchitis, fowl plague, Mareks disease – a form of cancer – and infectious throat disease.

The pharmaceutical farmyard brings its own ethical problems, closely linked to those of the growing use of transgenic animals in laboratory research. In both areas genetic engineering could and should mean the end of a lot of suffering. Farm animals killed for meat could and should be steadily replaced by mammalian cell cultures (of the kinds grown to clone pharmaceuticals) with added genes for flavour and consistency. Beef could have built-in horseraddish or mustard, lamb built-in mint flavouring. Cell cultures could be increasingly used for research, animals with no higher brain centres for consciousness might be specially bred, by manipulating genes controlling development, for use in laboratory research for which cell cultures or organs grown outside the body could not be used because experiments need whole animals.

My own feeling is that experiments which involve the use of intelligent, conscious animals will be gradually outlawed by public revulsion, as research increasingly makes us aware of the fact that we are just another animal with a bit more brain than the others. But there are disturbing possibilities; wingless or featherless chickens, animals given low intelligence to make them more docile in factory farm conditions, mice with giant spleens used as hyper-productive monoclonal antibody factories, mice whose lives are entirely painful and miserable because they develop human cancers almost at birth, sheep or cows which never see daylight because they are too valuable to let out while they produce superdrugs . . .

What is needed is not a halt to research and development. They can mean better lives for farm and laboratory animals. The need is for firm legislation, backed by strong public opinion, to direct the use of genetic engineering with animal rights as much as human benefits in mind. The best hope for animals lies in maximum openness, by the farming and research industries, about their methods and their treatment of animals. Public opinion could do the rest, so long as it is properly informed.

16

GREENING
INDUSTRY

Genetic engineering is changing medicine because it allows doctors to use the human body's natural chemical controls and messengers as drugs. They are far more potent and specific in their effects than conventional drugs. There is a parallel in industry. Enzymes, the natural catalysts found in all living things, can now be used to catalyse reactions in chemical industry. They, too, are much more potent and much more specific in their effects than man-made catalysts.

At present the numbers of reactions which can be catalysed by enzymes are limited by the supply of natural enzymes. But now that new ways to create new enzymes are being developed the numbers of enzyme-catalysed reactions – biotransformations – is due to increase by leaps and bounds.

Enzymes bring about all the complex chemical reactions going on in all living things. Enzymes are big, complex protein molecules, each produced according to the blueprint of a single gene. Over many millions of years, enzymes have evolved to become amazingly efficient at their tasks. They are able to make chemical reactions happen, as they must inside living animals and plants, at ordinary room temperatures and ordinary atmospheric pressure.

That long-evolved efficiency is a natural resource as real and ancient as coal or oil. But unlike fossil fuels, enzymes are renewable, potentially inexhaustible, and capable of further improvement through genetic engineering. Enzymes offer chemical industries safer, cleaner and, because they need no heating or pressurizing, cheaper ways of making products.

As recently as the 1970s, using enzymes on a large scale in industry was regarded as an unrealistic dream. But genetic engineering has changed all that. Before its advent enzymes had to be extracted expensively and messily from living cells. Now, by putting the gene for the required enzyme into a cell culture and cloning it, anyone can make as much of any enzyme as they want.

Cloning is one thing that is opening up industry to enzymes, the other thing is the good news that enzymes can be made to work in industrial environments. Enzymes work naturally in warm water thick with salts, sugars and proteins – the user-friendly environment of the living cell. But scientists are finding that some enzymes work surprisingly well out of water, in acids or alkalis or in organic liquids such as alcohol. And as we shall see, by making enzymes work in new chemical environments, it is possible to enlarge the range of reactions they can catalyse and so the range of tasks they can carry out in industry very greatly.

In the UK biologists and chemists saw the potential for the use of enzymes in industry which genetic engineering was bringing about in the mid-1980s. Enthusiasts from Warwick, Kent and Exeter Universities talked to Government scientists who shared their vision, and were prepared to match investment by industry with investment by Government. The outcome is the Biotransformations Centre, in which scientists of all three universities are exploring the uses of enzymes in industry.

One main use for biotransformations being explored by the Centre is in making chemicals in such a way that all their molecules are either left-handed or right-handed. The thalidomide tragedy, in which hundreds of babies were born with terribly crippled limbs, would never had happened if the drug involved had been made not by conventional chemistry but by enzymes. The thalidomide molecule can exist in two forms which are mirror images of each other, left and right-handed. One of these does the job the drug was designed to do, the other caused the abnormalities. Conventional chemistry makes a mix of both forms. But there is an enzyme which makes only the wanted form.

Substances whose molecules are made so they are all right-handed or all left-handed are called homochiral. Left-handedness or right-handedness is known as chirality. The consequences of making a chemical product which is heterochiral – part left-handed and part right-handed – may not be as drastic as in the case of thalidomide. But very often the reaction which the product is required to perform – inside the human body if it's a drug, or inside a weed if it's a herbicide, or inside an insect's body if it's an insecticide – will not happen if the chemical is made with the wrong chirality.

This means that if the substance is made in the ordinary way, which produces a heterochiral mix, then half of it will be at best useless, at worst, as with thalidomide, very harmful. Because chemical reactions in living things must produce homochiral products, enzymes have evolved to provide them. Using such enzymes in industry avoids wasteful making of harmful substances and saves money. Developing enzymes to make homochiral substances to use as drugs, pesticides, herbicides, food flavourings and perfumes are major preoccupations in research programmes such as those in the Biotransformations Centre.

Pollution control is an area where enzymes are in their element. Clean-ups can be tackled by whole living organisms, if necessary pepped up by genetic engineering, bred to feed on and to break down the pollutants. Alternatively the enzymes used can be cloned outside the organisms they normally work inside. Most organic chemical compounds (compounds based on chains or rings of carbon atoms, often with very complex molecules) are broken down naturally by bacteria which have evolved over many millions of years to feed on and break down living things when they die and sink into the soil. But every year industry devises thousands of new organic chemicals, which differ from those produced naturally by living processes. Because they are new there are no bacteria or other micro-organisms around able to break down the new chemicals.

Evolution will take many years to produce the enzymes needed naturally. Nature has been losing the battle to clean up pollution, she lacks the tools for the task and moves too slowly to devise new ones. If the battle is to be won, genetic engineers must take a hand and speed up evolution. Only then can living processes cope with the flood of new chemicals.

Dr Kenneth Timmis and his colleagues in Geneva University in Switzerland have been using genetic engineering to redesign soil bacteria to make them more able to feed on and break down man-made organic chemicals. They started with a toxic waste product of industry, 4 ethylbenzoate (4EB). One strain of a common bacterium, pseudomonas, which does live in the soil, turns out to possess an enzyme which does break down 4EB. Unfortunately this enzyme stops working almost as soon as it starts, because it is inactivated by one of the chemicals made by the breakdown of 4EB.

This looked a knotty problem. But it has been solved by a combination of selective breeding and genetic engineering. Bacteria with artificially induced genetic mutations, were created and tested by Dr Timmis until he found one strain which had an enzyme which broke down 4EB. Another had a similar enzyme which did something slightly different but was not inactivated by the breakdown product of 4EB. When the two genes for these two enzymes were both transferred into pseudomonas, their combined enzymes made it break down 4EB without being inactivated by breakdown products, so it went on until there was no 4EB left to destroy.

Scientists would love to use similar techniques to tackle what is probably the world's biggest single terrestrial pollution problem, the accumulation of polychlorinated biphenyls (PCBs). The excellent properties of PCBs used as insulators able to work at both high and low temperatures were realized over fifty years ago. Since then hundreds of millions of tons of these materials in worn-out electrical equipment have been dumped and have found their indestructible way into soil, water and the bodies of every kind of living creature. There they accumulate because no bacteria or any other micro-organism have yet evolved the enzymes needed to break PCBs down to harmless compounds.

Left to themselves, bacteria will eventually evolve strains able to break down PCBs, because analysis shows that between them the different bacteria have all the enzymes needed to break down each of the chemical bonds which hold PCB molecules together. Eventually, bacteria mating and exchanging genes at random, much as higher organisms do in sexual reproduction but much more quickly and easily will throw up a 'bug' with a combination of all the enzymes needed to break down PCBs. But those concerned about PCB pollution don't believe we can afford to wait that long. Dennis Focht, Professor of Cell Microbiology in the University of California at Riverside, doesn't think we have to wait. A combination of forced evolution and gentic engineering could provide the answer.

Professor Focht is using forced evolution to produce new strains of bacteria which feed on PCBs. He took two strains of bacteria, each with one of the enzymes needed to break down PCBs, grew them in cultures till the culture dishes overflowed and allowed the overflow to spill over from each culture and to flow down a glass tube packed with glass beads, down which also trickled a constant stream of mixed PCBs, the only source of food available to the mixed bacteria moving down the column.

The bacteria had to adapt or die, eat PCBs or starve. Only those bacteria which absorbed each other's genes for the enzymes needed to break down PCBs were able to feed on the PCBs. The rest starved to death. Within only one week Focht had produced strains which, while still not quite able to break down PCBs single-handed, were able to break down smaller molecules each representing about one-half of a PCB molecule. Focht believes it won't be long before he has produced strains able to break down PCBs completely. That could be the beginning of the end of the world's worst accumulation of toxic waste.

Once bacteria able to break PCBs down have been produced, their genes can be taken and introduced into other micro-organisms, chosen or designed to grow where PCBs have been dumped, so as to feed on and dispose of them. It has been argued that genetically engineered bacteria tend to be weaklings, unable to survive in competition with natural bacteria. But the sheer quantities of PCBs available for food should ensure that the genetically-engineered strains survive and flourish. They will have no competition for what, for them, will be a rich food source.

Even without genetic engineering, much can be done by searching for bacteria or fungi with wanted enzymes and getting them to mate with other species of bacteria which will live where the enzyme is needed. For example, the British company Biotechnica have cleaned up the site of a disused gasworks near Blackburn in Lancashire, by feeding samples of soil contaminated with phenols and coal tars to various members of the company's extensive collection of cultured bacteria, until they found bacteria which would clean up the soil by feeding on these pollutants.

Bacteria which like it hot are being eagerly sought. Several scientific teams from the USA and elsewhere are screening the natural hot springs of the world in search of thermophiles, bacteria which live naturally in such springs, because of their potential value in industry. Thermophiles have important potential advantages, for example in food industries. If thermophiles can be used to process cheap chemicals into exotic fats and oils used in cakes and chocolates, then the bacteria can carry out the necessary reactions at temperatures high enough to kill off any other bacteria in the food products, thus sterilizing them as they are made.

Dr David Hardman at the Biotechnology Centre at Kent University has already used genetic engineering to make thermophiles found in hot springs into living catalysts suitable for use in the food industry. One such hot spring bacterium, *Bacillus stearothermophilus*, can make fats for cakes and chocolates working at 65°C. At that temperature not only are other bacteria killed but there is no need to add chemical solvents to dissolve the fats, they melt anyway. So *B. stearothermophilus* makes foods free from risk of contamination with bacteria or chemicals – an attractive prospect in today's climate of concern about food hazards.

Unfortunately thermophiles are slow workers. Their fat-processing and other useful enzymes work much more slowly than those of bacteria which live at normal temperatures. This is because thermophiles normally devote most of their energy to protecting themselves against damage by overheating, leaving little to spare for processing fats. But David Hardman has used genetic engineering to speed them up. He has inserted several extra copies of the gene for a fat-processing enzyme into thermophiles, so that they are so plentifully supplied with the enzyme that they process fats as quickly as low-temperature bacteria.

To prevent the bacteria trying simply to get rid of the extra genes – an irritating habit of all genetically-engineered bacteria – Hardman used a clever trick. He linked the extra genes to other genes without which the thermophile can't feed, so that if the thermophile loses the added genes it starves. This way it keeps the extra genes and retains the ability to process fats at high temperatures.

Recently scientists have discovered bacteria which live naturally around the vents of volcanoes in the deep oceans. While first reports of their surviving temperatures of 200°C and even higher have been discounted, it's clear that there are high-temperature thermophiles down there. David Hardman and others are now considering the idea of bringing such bacteria to the surface to make use of them in chemical industry, to catalyse reactions which need both high temperatures and high pressures, the conditions found at the bottoms of the oceans.

Bacteria able to survive extreme cold rather than heat could be used to help to colonize the planet Mars. Mars is too cold for advanced life forms, as well as lacking oxygen. A first step in making Mars more habitable could be to seed it with bacteria which have been found in the Antarctic, living in the ice. Mars is warm enough to sustain them and has rich reserves of the minerals they need to feed on. Genetic engineering could make Antarctic bacteria still better adapted to a Martian environment. Perhaps they could be enabled to photosynthesize, or be combined with one-celled plants, so as to produce oxygen to enrich the Martian atmosphere for future colonists?

With a host of practical uses for bacteria and their enzymes appearing, now that the enzymes can be made in bulk outside the bacteria, and the bacteria improved by providing them with extra genes, the search for novel micro-organisms themselves in the soil, in hot springs and elsewhere is intensifying. Dr John Higgins, Director of the Cranfield Institute of Biotechnology, believes that far too little effort is going into the search for novel enzymes in environments other than hot springs. Higgins is searching instead for enzymes in tropical rain forests, because of the lush variety of organic chemicals and micro-organisms which feed on them to be found there – a far greater variety than are to be found in hot springs.

Higgins quotes ponds where wastes are dumped after extracting palm oil, where temperatures reach 90°C and more as foliage rots down in steaming compost in tropical heat. A huge variety of micro-organisms have evolved to take advantage of such conditions. Higgins has already identified some promising micro-organisms while working with colleagues in Thailand, Mexico and elsewhere. He sees them coming into use in industry in two or three years time.

Genetic switches which protect our own bodies against overheating are potentially valuable for industry. When we begin to overheat, a switch is thrown in the overheating cells which makes them produce special proteins, so called 'heat shock' proteins which protect against heat.

Scientists in the Battelle Institute in Geneva have uncoupled the switch, a sequence of DNA attached to the genes for heat shock proteins, which normally switches on the making of such proteins when the cell containing the genes heats up. They have coupled the switch to other genes instead and found it works equally well on them. When such combinations are inserted into cell cultures, the cultures only make whatever the gene is the blueprint for when the temperature of the culture is raised above that temperature to which the switch responds.

The cells engineered like this then make the product of the gene abundantly, because another function of the temperature switch sequence is to drive cells to make a lot of heat shock protein very quickly. So when the switch sequence is attached to a gene for a useful product, it provides a mechanism not only for controlling but for stimulating production of the product, simply by altering the temperature by a few degrees.

Temperature switches like this will be used to control the production of cloned substances by cell cultures in bioreactors. Like other control sequences being discovered, the switch works in any kind of living cell. It could be used to control and accelerate production in animal cell cultures as well as bacteria cultures.

17

IMMUNITY: A NEW FORCE IN INDUSTRY

The search for novel bacteria in hot springs or tropical forests is still turning up enzymes new to science. Enzymes put to work in strange chemical environments and required to feed on unfamiliar chemicals have proved to be unexpectedly adaptable. By placing an enzyme in a new chemical environment, in alcohol instead of water for example, it is even possible to make the enzyme work backwards. It then encourages what was originally the product of the reaction it catalysed to become the substrate, the starting point of the reaction, while the original starting point or points become the product. If this worked for every enzyme, it would effectively double the number of reactions they could catalyse.

But neither the intensity of the search for novel enzymes nor new tricks for making use of existing ones can hide the increasingly obvious fact that evolution has produced only a limited number of enzymes, a few thousand, for a limited number of purposes, and that the enzymes needed to catalyse most reactions used in chemical industry simply don't exist. Now, however, a revolutionary new technique is beginning to make it possible to create new enzymes to order, using the colossal resources of living things' natural defences against disease.

The immune system of a human, a mouse or any other animal is able to make literally millions of different antibodies. Each one is

177

a slightly different protein molecule, precisely shaped and with electric charges positioned to fasten itself onto just one other complex molecule, a protein foreign to the body defended by the antibodies, a foreign antigen on the surface of a bacterium or virus for example.

The remarkably specific and firm binding of an antibody with an antigen and the immune system's ability, through that precision, to differentiate between its own body and invading micro-organisms, is what defends us against disease. When an antibody becomes attached to an antigen the foreign organism carrying the antigen thereafter carries a tag which labels it for attack by T-cells, the cells which grapple with bacteria in hand-to-hand combat and destroy them by drilling holes in their outer membranes.

These two qualities of antibodies are now being exploited in a new way, by making antibodies into enzymes. This potentially makes it possible to make as many new enzymes as the number of antibodies the immune system of a mouse or rat can make. It could raise the numbers of enzymes available to industry from thousands to millions. It could be the decisive step which will make biotransformations, using enzymes, quiet, safe and economic, a great driving force in chemical industry, not just a small sector of it.

To understand how antibodies can be transformed into enzymes, we need to know first how enzymes work. A chemical reaction does not go straight from substance A to substance B. The reaction, at least if it involves chemicals of any degree of complexity, goes through an intermediate stage half way between A and B. This intermediate is called a transition state. It is a very energy-rich, very unstable state which exists for only a tiny fraction of a second.

A lot of energy has to be poured into substance A to make it change into the transition state. If you imagine the reaction as moving over a hill, then it has to be pushed uphill from substance A to the transition state, but from there to substance B it's downhill all the way.

What the molecule of an enzyme does is to push and pull the molecule of substance A towards the transition state, injecting energy into it and literally reshaping it. This is what happens as an enzyme molecule binds to a substrate molecule. It is as if the substrate is being forced into a sort of molecular corset, by the rigid shape of the enzyme molecule seizing hold of it and partially surrounding it. When the enzyme molecule releases the substrate molecule (which it does rapidly, so as to get hold of another one, catalysing a new reaction every fraction of a second) then the transition state the substrate has been forced into falls easily and quickly into the final state, which we called substance B.

The idea that this is how enzymes work was first proposed about twenty years ago. It is still not finally proved, because of the great difficulty of actually seeing a reaction pass through the brief and unstable transition state. But most chemists are more or less convinced that the theory is correct.

When an antibody reacts with an antigen, it reacts with it as tightly and as strongly as an enzyme with its substrate. An enzyme and an antibody are quite similar to look at. Each is a big complex protein molecule, a single strand but tangled into a precise three-dimensional shape. The sequence of DNA along the gene for building an enzyme or an antibody specifies with absolute precision the sequence of the corresponding chemical sub-units along the long-chain molecule of the antibody or enzyme. The sequence in which these sub-units, called amino acids, are arranged along the molecule made up from them, is what determines how the long protein molecule will curl up on itself and form a tangled but precise three-dimensional shape.

This three-dimensional shape is as precise and fixed as the sequence of amino acids along the molecule. It is the three-dimensional shape of the reactive site, of the small but all-important part of the antibody or enzyme molecule which actually binds to one specific antigen or substrate, which is vital.

Two teams of scientists in the USA, led by Peter Schultz of the University of California at Berkeley and Alfonso Tramontano of the Scripps Research Institute are enthused with the idea of making new enzymes out of antibodies. It is being done like this. Take a deep breath.

First they work out the structure of the transition state in a reaction which isn't catalysed by any natural enzymes. Then they synthesize the guessed-at transition state in the lab and – this is the vital step – inject it into a mouse. The mouse makes an antibody against the transition state. This antibody has a reactive site which conforms to the shape of the transition state it binds against. Then the scientists go through the usual procedure for making monoclonal antibodies. They immortalize the cells from the mice which are making the wanted antibody, and isolate and purify some of the antibody.

Then the antibody is mixed with the substrate which the scientists hope to persuade to undergo the wanted reaction. The aim is to make it first climb the hill to the transition state, then go down the other side into the end product of the reaction. The antibody molecule is waiting to cling to a corresponding transition state molecule, but there isn't one there. But there is the not-too-different substrate molecule. So, the reactive site of the antibody molecule pulls and pushes at the substrate molecule until it has persuaded it into the right shape. Lo and behold, the antibody has behaved just like an enzyme. The hard bit of the reaction is done and the transition state is all ready to toboggan downhill to the end product.

If it was as simple as that to make a new enzyme to catalyse a reaction, just by synthesizing the appropriate transition state and injecting it into a mouse, then abzymes, as antibodies made to work as enzymes are now being called, would by now be marching into industry with colours flying. But it isn't. The big problem is that transition states are so elusive that they can only be guessed at. And even if scientists guess correctly, because a transition state is by definition unstable, it can never be made to last long enough to inject into a mouse. Something stable enough for that but like enough to the real thing to stimulate the making of the right sort of antibodies is needed – not an easy compromise to find.

Even if the scientists guessing a transition state get the shape of the molecule exactly right, they are unlikely to get the charge distribution exactly right. The charge distribution is simply the way in which positive and negative electrical charges are distributed around the jigsaw-shaped surface of the transition state molecule. An abzyme molecule and the transition stage molecule it fastens to are attracted and held together all over their meeting surfaces by electrical forces. Unless the charges are in the right places, the forces won't be there and the abzyme and its substrate won't cling tightly together.

So there are these big problems in making antibodies work as enzymes. It's difficult to guess at something that can't be seen. It's difficult to make a different, more stable but still recognizable version of it. And there's the further difficulty of putting all the electrical charges in the right places. Between them these problems have severely limited the success of attempts to make working abzymes. Nonetheless, they have been made. Both the Berkeley and Alfonso teams have made antibodies to their best guesses of the transition states of chemical reactions, and used the antibodies as abzymes to catalyse the reactions. They have shown that they happened about a hundred thousand times faster than they would have without the abzyme.

That's a good start but there's still some way to go. To approach the efficiency of real enzymes, abzymes have to make the reactions they catalyse go a hundred times faster than the best so far. The reactions chosen for catalysis by the first abzymes were, understandably, reactions which are rather trigger-happy; they don't need much persuading to happen. But several working abzymes have now been made.

The worst problems in making abzymes are in trying to imitate transition states, first guessing at their structure and then making a molecule which is close enough to the real thing to create the right shaped antibody, but dissimilar enough to be stable. Genetic engineering provides what looks like being a way to bypass the problem. The idea is to make an antibody not to a guessed-at transition state but to the original substrate. Then, by fiddling around with the gene for this antibody, making tiny changes to individual bases in its DNA so as to produce a very slightly different antibody, it should be possible to produce an antibody which reacts not with the substrate but with the transition state. The altered antibody would be produced by implanting the altered gene into a new cell culture and cloning it.

This approach is only just beginning, because being able to pursue it means knowing how to alter genes so that the molecules they are blueprints for, enzymes and antibodies in this case, are changed to do a new job or do their old job better. This is what is called protein engineering, and it involves knowing how small changes in the sequence of DNA are going to affect the way in which the amino acids of the long-chain protein molecule make it curl up into a tangled ball.

A world leader in protein engineering is Professor Alan Fersht of the Cambridge Chemical Laboratory. Alan Fersht plans to engineer antibody genes to make the antibodies into abzymes which will react specifically with transition states. So here the two great biotechnologies, monoclonal antibodies and genetic engineering, that together are bringing about the revolution of 'Gene

181

Shifting', are once again working intimately together in partnership.

Are abzymes going to have a great industrial future in biotransformations? For a while yes, the enthusiasts believe. But in only perhaps twenty years time abzymes may be out of date. Alan Fersht believes that as protein engineers like him learn how to change genes so as to change enzymes as required, abzymes will become redundant. Instead of making an antibody to use as an enzyme to catalyse a reaction for which no natural enzyme exists, the company in need of the new enzyme will call in a protein engineer. He or she will design an enzyme to react with the hypothetical transition state of the reaction. Then he or she will go away and design a gene to make that enzyme, synthesize it, and clone it and the enzyme. Synthesizing a gene is a laborious business. But it only has to be done once. After that, cloning does the rest. Designer enzymes will have arrived.

But that is further ahead. Abzymes may be out of date in 2025 AD, but in 2000 AD they are likely to be finding many uses as new research tools and new medical drugs. A first use for abzymes is expected to be as enzymes able to break up big protein molecules at carefully selected points, so as to allow scientists to learn more about them. Other abzymes will be made which chop up DNA in the same way. This will facilitate the dissection of genes and help, among other things, in sequencing the human genome faster.

The point about this is that the natural enzymes that chop up DNA, known as restriction enzymes, are extraordinarily valuable in research. Being able to make more of them to chop up DNA molecules in ways that natural enzymes can't chop them will greatly accelerate the progress of research in human gene sequencing and genetic engineering.

Beyond the lab are uses in medicine. American groups are already working on abzymes designed to break down the proteins which form blood clots. The idea is to use abzymes as anti-clotting drugs which would be more effective than existing anti-clotting agents, because they would have all the built-in efficiency of antibodies and enzymes. Beyond that again is the exciting prospect of being able to make abzymes as reagents to break down any chosen tissue in the body. Hardened arteries? Ugly scar tissue? 'Port wine' disfigurements? Corns? Cancers? Abzymes could perhaps be made to attack them all. So they must have a considerable future in medicine. But in the end chemical industry will surely be the largest customer for abzymes, because of the unanswerable economic case for using enzymes to catalyse reactions. Once enzymes can be made to order, the lower cost and greater safety they provide will surely make them more and more widely used.

18
THE FURTHER
FUTURE

Where will genetic engineering have taken us in three hundred years time? To other planets, probably including other solar systems, for a start. Protein engineers, building on the examples of hot spring or Antarctic bacteria and others feeding on unlikely chemicals, will have designed living micro-organisims able to survive on Mars, on the Moon, even on Venus, in the clouds of Jupiter and on its moons. The invaders sent to Mars will be used to prepare the planet for human colonization, producing oxygen and water.

If the rich nations keep on getting richer, they could afford an altruistic experiment. They could send man-made life forms such as incredibly tough spores out into space in unmanned spore-sprinklers, targetted to planets in orbit around nearby stars. One or two planetary systems which might be suitable have been discovered recently. There could be no guarantee that the DNA in such spores would ever evolve mechanisms as intelligent as humans to replicate itself, but it might. Certainly, genetic and protein engineering make the idea of colonizing other planets a lot more realistic.

There has been much discussion of the possibility of cloning humans. That is replacing the nucleus of a fertilized human egg cell with a nucleus from a body cell of some person chosen for perpetuation. It has been done in lower animals and will soon be possible for humans, if it isn't already. But it's hard to see who could benefit. A dictator would not achieve personal immortality by cloning. Conventional eugenics, with perhaps DNA testing added on, and various permutations arising from today's ability to separate sex from reproduction, seem more likely routes for a dictator trying to create a master race or, for that matter, for well-off parents trying to perpetuate their genes and improve on them for their children's sakes.

For example, women will be able to give birth to identical genetic copies of themselves by dividing fertilized eggs in two, replacing one half to develop and be born, and keeping the other in deep freeze. The woman who grows from the first half-egg could have the second implanted into her womb when she came of child-bearing age. Men may wish to have babies, because their wives cannot bear children, because they want to share the experience and hard work of pregnancy and childbirth, or because they live in a stable homosexual relationship and want to enlarge it with children. Australian doctors are convinced it will be possible and several men have already put their names down, as hopeful fa-mothers. Lesbian couples may wish to have children with both partners' genes mingled by genetic engineering – taking a fertilized egg, replacing its nucleus with one from one partner's skin cell, adding in genes from the other partner and replacing the egg to develop . . .

Eventually single women as well as couples may shop around in embryo supermarkets where embryos are stored in deep freeze, carefully indexed and referenced with photographs of their genetic parents. Among the customers will be couples in search of embryos guaranteed free of genetic defects, later others in search of embryos of high intelligence to provide for their old age, in a world in which IQ will be increasingly vital. Young career women could deposit their embryos, with fathers carefully chosen and come back in their forties to take one embryo away to bear, with none of the higher risks of foetal defects attending normal parenthood later in life, selling the other two or three embryos to the supermarket to await another buyer. All the above possibilities seem more realistic to me than dictators cloning themselves.

The animal world could benefit vastly from genetic engineering. Factory farming could be done away with by the creation of brainless cell-cultured beef, pork and lamb. We could repay some of the debt we owe to farm animals by establishing colonies of sheep, pigs, cows and the rest and allowing them to live natural lives, with genes added only for such things as disease resistance or extra intelligence. The same could be true of dogs and cats, animals which have become friends and partners. As a one-time cat breeder I known how much feline intelligence varies. If breeders were to breed for that, instead of silly show points for a few generations, allying breeding to beneficial genetic engineering, then supercats which would be even more a joy to share a life with could be developed.

(Animals' hunting instincts could not be destroyed without destroying their personalities. But they could be redirected, to pursue electronic mice! So could the, less excusable, human hunting instincts. Robotic prey could replace the real thing, made suitably fearsome and evasive. Robots for 'sporting' hunters to pursue could include bigger game than any alive today – a recreated Tyrannosaurus Rex for example.)

II's not impossible to envisage superhens and supersheep with higher IQs made able to communicate by new electronic communicators happily providing eggs, wool, milk and cheese in exchange for food, shelter, protection and affection. Much research using laboratory animals, as well as factory farming, will I think become harder to justify as more and more research makes it clear that whether or not humans possess immortal souls, there is nothing more than a bit of extra brain power to distinguish humankind from other animals.

A growing priority for genetic engineering will be the creation of living substitutes for animals for research – human-type organisms or parts or organisms which mimic human biochemistry but have no consciousness. Since experiments involving conscious animals are already the most problematic, they may be finally outlawed. If superdogs and cats become still more intelligent, then it is open to question how long experiments on higher animals could survive their reproaches.

If animals can share some of our intelligence, we may want to share some of their qualities too. The human genes for body hair must still be there, waiting to be reawakened. Whether we lost our hair to keep cool when hunting, or during an aquatic stage in our evolution, or for some other reason, we still have tiny hairs left on our bodies. The appropriate stimulus could reawaken the hairy genes and reclothe us with luxurious pelts, which could form the bases of wholly new fashions.

Luxuriously pelted humans could, if they wished, walk among dinosaurs, mammoths and other creatures recreated by genetic engineering in future wildlife parks. A combination of cloning and protein engineering will make it possible to extract nuclei with partially-preserved DNA from frozen mammoth carcasses from Siberia and add in reconstructed versions of the genes that are missing. Then these nuclei could be inserted to replace those of fertilized elephant egg cells. Two years later the mother would give birth to an unusual, hairy offspring.

Will genetic engineering make us immortal? In the conventional sense, i.e. by making immortal humans, probably not. Limited life span is so innate to our cells and organs that we would have to be fundamentally redesigned to live forever, or even for three or four hundred years. Immortal organisms would have to be a product more of original protein engineering, than remodelled humanity. Brains, hearts and other organs that have fixed life-spans would have to be supplied with pools of eternally dividing new cells to draw on, like the lining of our gut and our bone marrow.

Old science fiction ideas of transferring human personalities into computers are out of date now that brain research has revealed how infinitely more complex the connections between brain cells are than those between silicon chips. We may be able to invent potentially immortal, intelligent, conscious flesh and blood creatures and give them some of our characteristics, some of our own genes even. But I don't think they'll be us.

Anyone who has ever tried to forecast a scientific or medical future even twenty years ahead knows what a hopeless task it is. Very possibly none of the above will happen. But genetic engineering will change the world somehow. Already in a few short years it has changed us from being the servants of our genes into being the masters, and potentially the reshapers, not only of them, but of all other life on Earth. Sceptre and crown have been suddenly thrust into the hands of a subject race. We have no choice but to ascend the throne, and reign.

APPENDIX:
HOW DNA WORKS

Various properties of DNA have been referred to briefly in other chapters, as and when they were relevant. This appendix attempts to sum up briefly how DNA works. How does it replicate itself? What happens when a gene is expressed, when DNA is transcribed into messenger RNA and translated into protein? It also aims to explain how DNA is manipulated by genetic engineers so as to transfer it from one living thing to another, or to use it to diagnose genetic diseases and, later, to attempt to cure them.

The genetic blueprints for making living things are made of DNA. They are handed on from generation to generation, so that, for example, children resemble their parents. The long thread-like molecules of DNA are tightly coiled inside all the twenty-three pairs of chromosomes, the microscopic rods of genetic material inside the nuclei of every cell in the human body. The chromosomes and the DNA inside them are identical in every one of all the billions of cells in each individual's body; brain cells, blood cells, bone cells and the rest. Only a fraction of the DNA in any one cell is active, only a small proportion of its blueprints are being translated into protein at any one time. This is why cells in one body differ from one another. Although they all have the same DNA, so as to renew a cell's structure or to make its products, different bits of the DNA are being expressed in different cells at different times.

Genes, meaningful bits of DNA each representing the blueprint for making one single protein molecule, perhaps an enzyme, perhaps part of a cell membrane, perhaps a hormone or an antibody for example, are dotted along the lengths of the strands of DNA in living cells. Only a few per cent of human DNA is actually made up of working genes, the products of which are made at some time in one or another cell of the body. Nearly all human DNA is made either of non-functioning genes, or of DNA with no known function except to act as a spacer between the genes.

DNA molecules inside the nuclei of cells, where the genetic blueprints are stored, are formed into the famous double helix shape, like long spiral ladders. Each side of the ladder is made of a long chain of molecules (sugar phosphates) which play no part in heredity. It is the rungs of the ladder that represent the genetic code. Half of each rung is contributed by one side of the ladder and half by the other. Each half of each rung is a chemical grouping called a base, quite a small and simple molecule. There are only four of these bases; adenine, thymine, guanine and cytosine. Because of their chemical properties, adenine will pair only with thymine and guanine with cytosine. So every rung of DNA's spiral ladder is made either of an adenine-thymine or of a cytosine-guanine pair.

This means that DNA is self-replicating. Suppose the double spiral is pulled apart, leaving each half of the ladder with its own bases, its half of each rung of the ladder, attached to it. Then each half of the ladder will re-assemble the other half along its length, given a supply of free-floating individual bases to build a new half-ladder. The individual bases will separately be attracted to and become attached to the right places opposite their opposite numbers along each single strand of DNA. A half-rung of thymine will be joined by a half-rung of adenine, a half-rung of guanine by a half-rung of cytosine, and so on. Then all the separate half-rungs, which have come to join the half-rungs forming one side of the ladder, themselves join up, and form the other side of the ladder. And there's a new complete double spiral. This is what happens when a cell divides to form two cells, each of which needs its full complement of DNA. The same thing happens to the other half of the original double spiral which has unwound.

Genes are stretches of DNA usually between 1000 and 2000 bases long, with much longer stretches of meaningless DNA between them. There are roughly 100,000 genes in any human cell. When a gene is expressed – makes its product – the two strands of the pair of the DNA double ladders forming that gene untwist and separate, leaving two single spirals each with rungs sticking out of it along its length. Each rung is a base. As in the duplication of DNA, complementary individual bases then come to attach themselves to their opposite numbers, forming the other half of the ladder anew.

But unlike the duplication of DNA, when a gene is expressed the DNA only untwists for the length of the thousand-odd bases representing the gene. The complementary strands formed do not remain attached to their partners but break away and travel out of the nucleus, through the membrane surrounding it, into the cytoplasm, the outer part of the cell. They are messengers, telling the cell to make the proteins for which the genes they come from are the blueprints.

When the bit of DNA that is the gene to be expressed untwists and its strands separate, one strand carries the bases in the right order to specify the message to make the protein. The other strand carries bases in a meaningless order. Their sequence depends on which of them attach themselves to the complementary bases along the first strand.

A new complimentary strand is formed alongside the meaningful strand of DNA. This new strand is made of RNA and is sent out into the cell as the DNA's messenger.

The messenger is transported to microscopic structures, organelles called ribosomes which make new proteins. There messenger RNA is translated into the protein for which its original gene is the blueprint. Like the RNA, the protein is a long-chain molecule made up of relatively few sub-units arranged in many different sequences. There are twenty protein sub-units, called amino acids. Starting at one end of the messenger RNA molecule, the first three bases along its length represent one amino acid at the start of the protein molecule which is to be made. The next triplet of bases define the second amino acid along the new protein chain. And so on.

A series of ribosomes move along each messenger, one after another, each one building a protein molecule, translating RNA's message into protein. The ribosome starts off at the beginning of the messenger with the first triplet. The appropriate amino acid is brought to its place opposite the triplet by a molecule called transfer RNA, which consists of another triplet of bases which are complementary to those on the messenger and so are attracted to and become attached to it. Each transfer RNA molecule brings one amino acid molecule to rest opposite its appropriate triplet on the messenger.

When that has happened, the ribosome moves along to the next triplet, and the process is repeated, with another amino acid coded for by the next triplet. In this way, as the ribosome moves along the messenger, it builds up, amino acid by amino acid, a corresponding protein alongside it. When the protein is complete, a triplet at the end of the messenger says 'stop'. And the complete molecule moves off into the cell (carefully guided to the place where it is needed by the cell's still-little-understood transport system).

All DNA looks the same under the most powerful microscope. So how do genetic engineers isolate individual genes for cloning to make large numbers of copies of the genes? The answer is that the scientists use enzymes which naturally cut DNA strands at precise points, at particular sequences of bases. These enzymes are called restriction enzymes. There are well over 150 of them available for use.

Once DNA has been cut up by an enzyme, it can be sorted and the wanted bits picked out in several ways. Centrifuging can separate bits of different sizes and weights. Electric fields can be used to pull bits of DNA through jelly. Pieces move at different rates according to their sizes and finish up in different positions on the jelly.

Once the wanted genes or parts of genes have been isolated they have to be inserted into bacteria, or other cell cultures, sometimes yeasts, occasionally mammalian cell cultures, to be cloned. This is usually done by taking small ring-shaped bits of bacteria DNA called plasmids, which carry part of the bacterium's own DNA outside its nucleus, and cutting the ring open with restriction enzymes. The bits of DNA to be cloned are added and more enzymes used to make the joins heal, so the extra DNA is spliced into the plasmid. Then the plasmid is put back into the bacterium.

The fact that the bases along any sequences of DNA attract and cleave to their corresponding bases; adenine to thymine, guanine to cytosine; means that if a sequence of DNA which is complementary to another sequence is placed in a solution containing lots of bits of assorted DNA, the complementary sequence will attach itself to the added sequence. This is now a very well-established way of looking for and picking out any wanted sequences of DNA. The sequence used to search for its complementary sequence is called a DNA probe. DNA probes can be used to search out complementary sequences representing defective genes. In this way, DNA probes are being increasingly used to diagnose defects in foetuses at a very early stage, by seeing if a defect is present in DNA from a tiny specimen of tissue taken from the foetus.

Restriction enzymes are also used in plant and animal genetic engineering and will be used in human gene therapy. The enzymes are used to splice human genes into viruses which naturally insert their own genes into human, plant or animal DNA. Then the virus is allowed to infect the animal, plant or human in need of improvement. It introduces the human genes into cells along with its own genes.

All living things with the exception of a large minority of viruses store their genetic blueprints in the form of DNA. Some viruses store it as RNA. These viruses may have evolved from messenger RNA since, like it, they are single-stranded. In order to be passed on from generation to generation of the cells they infect, the viruses employ an enzyme which copies their RNA blueprint into the form of DNA, so it can be integrated into the cell's own DNA. This enzyme is called reverse transcriptase, because its function is the reverse of transcription, the term used to describe the turning of a DNA message into the form of messenger RNA. Reverse transcriptases borrowed from viruses are now very widely used by genetic engineers.

FURTHER READING

Genetic Engineering for Almost Everybody   William Bains
   (Penguin)

The Blind Watchmaker   Richard Dawkins   (Longman)

The Selfish Gene   Richard Dawkins   (Paladin)

What Sort of People Should There Be?   Jonathan Glover
   (Penguin)

In Search of the Double Helix   John Gribbin   (Gower)

Human Gene Therapy   Eva Nicholl   (Harvard University
Press)

Pirates of the Cell   Andrew Scott   (Basil Blackwell)

Food Crops for the Future   Colin Tudge   (Penguin)

The Double Helix   James Watson   (Penguin)

The New Genetics and Clinical Practise   Sir David Weatherall
   (Nuffield Provincial Hospitals Trust)

Setting Genes to Work   Stephanie Yanchinski   (Penguin)

Unnatural Selection   Edward Yoxen   (Heinemann)

Future Earth   edited by Nigel Calder and John Newell
   (Christopher Helm)

INDEX